395

# An
# American
# Woman
# &
# Alcohol

PATRICIA
KENT

# An
# American
# Woman
# &
# Alcohol

HOLT,
RINEHART
AND WINSTON

NEW YORK
CHICAGO
SAN FRANCISCO

Library of Congress Catalog Card Number: 66–22203

Third Printing, April, 1974

Designer: Ernst Reichl

ISBN: 0–03–060425–7

Printed in the United States of America

# Contents

For my husband,

without whom I would not be

in any way alive!

# You,
# Too,
# Can
# Be
# an
# Alcoholic

# I

# The

# Beginning

THE ad in the liquor store window read: "Welcome to the Grownup's Hour!" This amused me, because the one thing you are not, if you drink to excess, is a grownup!

Dependence on alcohol can start anytime in life—and anywhere. It can begin in a private prep school in the Connecticut hills or in a dirty, shared kitchen in Watts, Los Angeles. Alcohol, like death and taxes, is the great leveler.

What is alcoholism? Who is an alcoholic? Alcoholism is a serious illness, an addiction to alcohol. It is also host to many other diseases. It is considered by many doctors to be the next highest disabler and killer after cancer and heart disease. Alcoholism, very simply, is individual reaction to stress.

Physically, a woman becomes alcoholic by drinking. No matter how neurotic a woman is, if she doesn't

3

drink, she cannot and does not become an alcoholic. Yet, it is possible to be alcoholic from the very first drink.

But everyone does not react to daily stress by drinking or by taking pills, the tranquilizers and barbiturates that are the twin crutches of some women's lives. Alcohol and pill-taking are really part of the same problem. And the end result of addiction to either is the same. Make no mistake about it. You stop drinking, stop taking pep pills and sleeping pills, stop leaning on those crutches, or you finish in a mental institution or the grave—an early one!

How does a nice girl get to be a drunk? It is important to know this, so you can catch and arrest the disease early. No longer is it necessary to go the whole route. No longer is it a hopeless slide straight to the bottom from too many drinks at parties, through hiding bottles in the bedroom, through sanitariums and city hospitals to state institutions and death.

It may help to know that alcoholics are often smarter, more sensitive, and more decent than many other people. If a woman drinks to excess she is scared and running. She is finding surcease, relief from pain and guilt, temporary anesthesia, escape. She is refusing to face reality. I have never known an alcoholic woman who was a deliberate destroyer of other people. She may have appeared so to others, but, in reality, she wished to destroy only herself.

If you are worried about your drinking, it is a good indication that you have an alcoholic problem. If this book has one purpose, one reason, it is to show that drinkers do not have to ruin their lives through alcohol and pills. It is not a medical book nor a social study nor advice from a psychiatrist or a priest, but a book

4

for girls and women facing the ghastly pressures of everyday American living. A book for women from fifteen to eighty, who aren't making it in their worlds, who need help.

Stop now before it's too late. Get help. Alcoholism is a disease, not a lack of courage and morality. If you are addicted, will power to stop drinking has nothing to do with your problem. No one has more will power than an alcoholic with a murderous, unfunny, sick, degrading hangover trying to get to the office or to school. Incidentally, in the beginning, most alcoholics do *not* have hangovers. They also do not get drunk very quickly. Their capacity for drinking is enormous; they often drive everyone else home. A normal drinker will admit to a hangover. An alcoholic almost never will. Secretiveness and deception become a way of life. Taking sedatives to cure hangovers is the next easy step. Benzedrine to get going, phenobarbitol to sleep is the pattern and the beginning of the slide. And it only goes one way—down.

Socially, it is very easy to become an alcoholic today. *The* way of life in America is drinking. At a party, prom, luncheon, dinner, or dance the first thing thrust upon you is a drink. If you want to be a "swinger" you drink. No man wants to take out a "square." So you drink. You can't have lunch with a client unless you drink with him. When the bridge club comes, it is so gauche to serve coffee. After a golf match head for the lounge. What are you going to do, go right home? And, if you live alone, you're *entitled* to a drink after a hard day. If you don't live alone you're entitled to share the *release* of alcohol.

If you are an American woman trying to make today's "scene" you are a sitting duck for the disease of

5

alcoholism. Not everyone contracts it, of course, but your chances of succumbing to this illness, and/or to pill addiction, are good. There are hundreds of thousands of unsuspected and unsuspecting alcoholic women of all ages living half-lives all over this land.

There are many avenues to alcohol addiction. One of the most serious symptoms of alcoholism is the inability, refusal, or unwillingness to admit the existence of the disease. The ability to rationalize to oneself and others is indigenous to alcoholics and pill addicts, and often prevents the alcoholic from getting help until the disease has noticeably progressed.

One woman I know, from an excellent family background, married a minister and never touched a drop of alcohol until she was fifty-five. She was the leader of her community in civic and church activities. Then her husband died. After a suitable interval she married the president of the bank, a widower. She had a series of minor illnesses and consulted her doctor. He recommended sherry for her nerves, a simple cocktail in the evening before dinner.

Surprisingly, she loved it. Soon one sherry became two, two became four; and she began to drink during the day. Her drinking progressed to morning drinks, drinking at the wrong time, showing up drunk at dinner parties, to around the clock drinking. She could not admit to herself or anyone else that a woman of her ability and background could be alcoholic. Today, at seventy, she has not left her house for three years and is a total invalid, depending entirely on the ministrations of husband and servants to keep her alive.

She is a physio-chemical alcoholic, someone physiologically addicted to liquor from the first drink. She was allergic to alcohol, yet her body craved it. The weakness may have been inherited; it may have been a simple chemical reaction of her body.

Many doctors reject the physical theory of addiction, contending there must always be an underlying psychological reason. They may be right. But I have known too many women who started down the road to alcoholism straight from their first drink not to include physiochemical reaction as a possibility here.

If you drink, and you have a physical reaction, even —or especially—if you don't drink much, chances are you are allergic to alcohol and should quit—right now, before it is too late. Because one thing is sure in alcoholism: Once you have the disease, it can only get worse. Alcoholism is progressive. You can arrest it, never cure it. Once an alcoholic, always an alcoholic.

You may know some people who drank sloppily and excessively at one time, then just tapered off and now drink "normally." They are few and far between. They were *not* alcoholic in the first place. If you choose to experiment, and the choice is yours alone, go right ahead. You may not be alcoholic; but the odds are against you. Your "experiment" may cost you your looks, your job, perhaps your husband and children, and possibly your life. And you will have proven something that you secretly have known all along, but won't admit. You are an alcoholic.

Emotionally, the alcoholic woman brings many problems to her first drink. An alcoholic is an emotional, spiritual, moral, often physical, and usually financial bankrupt. No matter how bad it is for a man, it is always worse for a woman! Society still exists on the double standard. Behavior accepted, or at least tolerated, in a man is scorned in a woman. She is still expected, modern thinking notwithstanding, to be the moral and social leader. When she falls, it is from a higher pedestal—and it is almost always to a lower depth. Men tend to drink openly; women drink secretively.

It is almost always more difficult for a woman to admit and accept that she is an alcoholic. It just couldn't happen to her! She is by her very nature more careful, more circumspect, more able to cope with problems than a man. She must give more, fight harder. And if and when she becomes alcoholic, it is with more of a vengeance.

Alcoholism is an insidious disease that seeks out the best. It is usually the woman who has a great deal to give to life, who thinks more, who loves more, who feels more, who needs more—and who drinks more and destroys more.

If you are getting a modicum of happiness and satisfaction from your everyday life, you do not *need* alcohol. It is a substitute, an escape. Alcohol drops a curtain over fear, guilt, and reality itself. If you use alcohol to avoid coping with your problems, you probably will become alcoholic. It is so much easier to reach for a drink than to reach down inside of yourself for the courage to face life. But alcohol solves nothing. If you are alcoholic, there is no problem that one drink won't make worse!

There are many emotional causes for alcoholism, probably as many causes as there are alcoholics. But there is one emotional symptom characteristic of *every* alcoholic: self-pity. *Every* woman drunk I know felt sorry for herself, with or without cause. Women alcoholics also commonly share great helpings of hostility and resentment. Their frustration point is very low.

A woman feels sorry for herself if she is an educated housewife with four screaming children, if she is a top advertising copywriter who sleeps with the client to keep her job, even if she is simply a high-school girl with acne. She feels sorry for herself if her husband, her reason for living, spends most of his daytime hours away at his job, and most of his evening hours worrying about it. She is hostile to the outside world. She resents men, other women, her husband's job, her children, people with money, the "beautiful" people—in short, everyone who is what she thinks she is not. She is grossly maladjusted; she is grossly immature. Her character defects ambush her into alcoholism.

Granted, this may all be covered up beautifully, for a time—with fine clothes, with good manners, compulsive volunteer work, men other than her husband, with anything and everything her rationalizing little soul can devise. But she is still left with her disease.

Very often the last person to recognize it or to admit it is herself. Husband, parents, friends, and employers may mention that she drinks too much. Then they tell her, and finally they nag. But it doesn't matter. Because with alcohol, she becomes what she is not, one of the beautiful people. The bottle is always half-full—never half-empty—for a time. It builds.

Spiritually, the incipient alcoholic woman is generally arid. By the time she reaches full-blown alcoholism, she usually doesn't believe in God, justice, mercy, or any of the virtues at all. The word "God" is anathema to her.

Oddly, there is one other type of alcoholic: the girl who prays in blind faith to be relieved of her agony. The girl who screams out in the night for help, when she feels she is destroying her own soul. But even she doesn't *really* believe God is there. And He is most certainly not listening to her.

9

Before women drunks become pathetic, gelatinous, vegetating creatures, they are usually the world's prize cynics. They know everything. There is nothing good in this world. Nothing good is ever going to happen to them. And because they are what they are, nothing good ever does. If it should, they wouldn't recognize it. Life is a snare and a delusion. At the least, it is vaguely depressing. At the worst, a horror.

However, if they do something about their disease and become sober belonging members of society, they awake one day in shock. Other people have problems, too. Everyone does not run away. Women alcoholics often, upon attaining sobriety, become better members of society than they ever were before. They become more aware; they begin to live more intensely, more knowingly. Their courage to cope with problems becomes the courage of enlightenment, the courage of understanding. This can be the new spiritual beginning.

# II

# Neuroses

ANXIETY is the bubonic plague of the twentieth century. Immaturity is its breeding ground, insecurity its symptom. These all play a major role in the development of an alcoholic. Anxiety begins with fear—fear of the unknown, fear of oneself, fear of people, fear of not measuring up, fear of living. Anxiety is fear squashed down inside of you, gnawing at your insides, your organs, your loves, your emotions, screaming to get out. If anxiety becomes powerful enough, overwhelming enough, and it often does, the person whom it possesses may become suicidal. Life does not hold enough joy, enough adventure for you to overcome that all-pervading sense of hopelessness and fear. Living, life itself, cannot beat out anxiety.

In many ways we each dig our own grave. Probably alcoholism and addiction to pills are forms of the death wish. Logically taken, if you accept the premise that an alcoholic is often smarter and more sensitive than most people, she should know enough intellectually not to destroy everything she is through alcohol and barbiturates. Yet, it is not the intellect that motivates her to drink. She is emotionally compulsive about her drinking and pill-taking. She simply cannot leave alcohol alone. She realizes it is killing everything she is, everything she hoped to be. But she cannot stop. Isn't this a secret death wish, a wish to remove herself from the battlefield of life, without the bravado to do it in one grand gesture?

Yet, in reality, alcohol only prolongs the agony, only increases the anxiety, only makes everything a whole lot worse. When you are an alcoholic your guilt increases a thousandfold. You become the prey of every accusation, the butt of every sordid joke, the mistake in everyone's environment. Alcohol doesn't deaden anxiety; it only channels it. Through alcohol, you become anxiety's child.

Where does this anxiety come from? What brings a "normal" American girl with every advantage, a healthy, pretty, well-educated female to the brink of alcoholic destruction? And, surprisingly enough, many alcoholic women I know *are* quite beautiful. Lovely enough, poised enough, educated enough to be the envy of many of their friends. What happened? Many personalities fit into the alcoholic pattern. But there are some who have a greater tendency to become alcoholic than others. The main reason is emotional immaturity. Some girls are mature at fifteen; some women are children at sixty.

What is maturity? The dictionary defines maturity as completeness of growth and development, fully worked out, perfected. I define it as an acceptance of who you are and what you are, coupled with a strong sense of responsibility toward yourself and others.

Mothers play an enormous role in the maturation of their children. It is no accident that the baby bottle full of milk often turns into the bottle full of scotch or seconal. Here are some self-explanatory questions relating to maturity:

Are you afraid to leave your mother's house?

Do you depend on your family for strength, aid, and encouragement?

Do you defy your mother, telling yourself "you'll show her," but secretly glad she's there to discipline you?

If you're over eighteen, do you turn down dates to stay home with mother?

Do you feel you would be deserting her, if you were to marry?

If you are married, do you call her every day or fly to her with every problem?

Or, on the other side of the coin, are you willing to, or have you, married in haste—perhaps the first boy who came along—to "show" your family?

Is your heart bound up in old and aging relationships, safe ones, which demand little or nothing of you?

Are you unwilling, even vaguely so, to meet new friends, try something new, give of yourself a little?

Are the relationships in which you are most at ease those you made in school?

Are you afraid to take your place in society, to

13

fight for your rights and the respect due you
from others?

Do you isolate yourself, physically, or emotionally,
to avoid being hurt?

Do you react badly to responsibility?

Do you expect other people to undo your mistakes,
if you say you're sorry?

If so, you are immature. You are in conflict with
yourself. And, if you choose to drink, you may already
be racing down the road to alcoholic dependence!

While the anxious and immature are often subject
to alcoholism, so, in many instances, is the girl in pain.
This does not mean physical pain which, of course, can
also happen and can open the door to barbiturate addiction. It means psychic pain. Pain so deep you often
cannot acknowledge its existence. You know something
terrible is happening to you; it hurts. So you drink to
blot it out. By drinking, you may instinctively be putting off something worse: a nervous breakdown, an ulcer,
a heart attack. Liquor is an anesthetic; it may be yours.

In some cases the psychic pain you are endeavoring
to ease may not be traumatic. It may not be a death, or
a broken marriage, or failure to get into college. It may
be something as simple as trying to get over your nerv-
ousness at a dance, or giving a dinner for your husband's boss, or playing in the tennis tournament. You're
nervous; you drink for "courage." It works the first
time. You've learned the remedy; you increase your
intake for future problems. Soon you are on the merry-
go-round. It's very easy to climb aboard.

Third in the alcohol-susceptible group is the girl
who hates herself. She may have had a very strict,
proper upbringing. She may constantly castigate herself

for the slightest error in behavior or demeanor, even though no one else notices it or feels it is important. She has not measured up to her own perfectionist standards. She probably suppresses her feelings of hostility, turns her resentment against herself—and drinks. She is, in all probability, also blessed with a "scrupulous" conscience, and is weighted down with guilt. She drinks to suppress the guilt, then continues to drink to suppress the added guilt of drinking. That's how easy it is!

Fourth is the spoiled-rotten girl. These are multiplying in America today. Mommy coddled her all her life; daddy denied her nothing. She was never frustrated in any really important way. But one day she is—by an outside force. A prettier, smarter girl appears in school. There is someone more competent where she works. Or her husband cannot give her the Rolls until next week. She will *not* be thwarted, so she drinks. Drinking blots out her frustrations—and besides she likes it. If her behavior can make those who love her squirm, so much the better. They deserve it, she feels. When this woman sobers up, she will probably find it very difficult indeed to become honest with herself.

Fifth are women whose basic immaturity and consequent hostility take sexual forms. They may be afraid of men; they may be nymphomaniacs; they may be lesbians. Strangely enough, in the alcoholic pattern these women are very much in the minority. Some of them dissipate their aggressive drives in jobs. How many women do you know who have to prove every day they are as good as, or better than, men? If they are married, some take it out on defenseless, ineffectual husbands or unsuspecting children. Or they may form alliances with other women. If they add alcohol to their other problems,

15

they can become very sick indeed, often in a public and very messy way. They should put themselves in the care of a good psychiatrist, when they stop drinking. Incidentally, and obviously, a psychiatrist can only help when he knows the truth. Sessions with the doctor while one is still drinking or taking pills are very often quite useless, because anyone in this condition does not know what the truth is. It is very important to stop drinking, and cut off the pills, before embarking on therapy or analysis.

The women described here are merely a few of the neurotic personalities prone to alcoholism, all of which may overlap. There are many other kinds of alcoholic problems. If you do not find your personality structure here, and you are having trouble with your drinking— or you are taking too many pills—do not lie to yourself. It is the very nature of your disease that you do so. If you put this section down with relief, telling yourself, "That's not me," you still may be very ill.

Some women just slip into alcoholism. They are attractive and ambitious. Often they are very capable. When their assets are not readily recognized, they may begin to drink. They may be frustrated and unhappy. They become disillusioned. They discover with a shock that in the big world, ethics is often a meaningless word. Morality is something they heard their mothers mention. Nice guys finish last. All that matters is money and success. If they meet any interesting men, they do not wish to marry. They are in "The Great Wasteland." Their rainbow-colored world turns to an ugly gray. They drink to color it "beautiful" again. They take pills to make it livable. They are addicted.

Other women succumb to pressures and tensions. Twentieth-century pressures are unceasing. Face it, they will continue to grow. Competition is fantastic. To live daily life in megalopolis is to meet hundreds of challenges. To pay the bills becomes overwhelming.

To hold a job, you may have to become a cheat, a liar, a phony, a plagiarist. To get into the "right" clubs, or to get your children into the "right" schools, you become a panderer, a toady, an entertainer of viragos, a snob. You may have to turn your back on family, background, religion, and decency. Cheating in school is not only accepted, it seems, it is often expected! The questions you go to sleep with are: "What have they done for me today?" and "Am I with it?" Only the truly mature and secure know they don't have to prove anything.

Is it any wonder some women can't cope? Some try to flee physically, into marriages, for example, both bad and good. Or into jobs abroad. And some flee psychically —into liquor, tranquilizers, barbiturates, sex, into sanitaria and suicide. Alcohol becomes promise and fulfillment. Alcohol becomes religion, when faith is dead. It is the substitute for the man you dreamed you would marry. It is the companion for your lonely hours, a substitute for love, a buffer against nagging in-laws. Alcohol is humor and joy and friendship. It is the answer to everything. But how can you live with it?

Sheila was the only daughter of a strict Irish Catholic household. She was adored by her mother, and to a certain degree by her father. Her mother gave her everything—beautiful clothes, a summer home, cars, dancing lessons, piano lessons, riding lessons, in short, everything that makes up the American Dream. She was well-educated in a series of small, exclusive convent schools. She graduated from college *magna cum laude* and went to graduate school. She was pretty and very popular.

However, unlike many spoiled girls, Shelia was ambi-

17

tious and willing to work to get what she wanted. Competition was an integral, searing part of her life. Much was expected of her; she was prepared to give it. She was also expected to make a "brilliant," suitable marriage.

On the surface her family was a normal, well-to-do functioning household. But underneath it was chaotic. Sheila's father drank, pretty much all of the time. Her mother compensated by taking over and running the family. Shelia was repeatedly warned not to marry a drinker but to marry a man who could give her the finer things in life. When she graduated from college she became engaged to a solid, upstanding Irish boy. His idea of life was a house in the suburbs and seven children; hers was trips to Europe, mink coats, and gracious entertaining. She was wise enough to see it wouldn't work and broke the engagement. She was ready for a flaming career.

She went into the communications business. Drinking is part of that industry's way of life. However, Sheila did not realize that most performers and executives do not drink to excess. They simply cannot afford to. It was a glamorous, gay life. She met many celebrities and drank with all of them. She also drank with anyone else who asked her to. She thought it was smart and fun. Alcohol was not a problem to her then, but later she told me she wondered what kind of a job she might have done had she been fully sober all the time. As it was, she performed adequately and was offered a better job by a network. She was twenty-three and thought she was on top of the world. She began to drink more. She never had lunch without a drink. She always went somewhere for cocktails after work. She began to be lonely. Her friends were all getting married; she was living at home with her family. The job did not measure up to what she had thought it would be; it became boring. Her father was drinking incessantly now, but it never cost him his job. Her mother was becoming ill and extremely demanding.

Sheila had two more engagements. One to a totally unsuitable delegate to the U.N., one to a very attractive emotional and financial leech. She was drinking all the time now, not caring very much what happened to her. She looked terrible, had gained a great deal of weight and cut her hair, and became quite careless about her appearance. Her world had turned gray; she could not cope with her problems, many of them self-made. She had demanded a great deal of herself; she could not measure up any more.

One day she created a ghastly scene at the network, secretly hoping to be fired. She was. But before she left, a man she had met there asked her to go to an Alcoholics Anonymous meeting with him. He knew she had a drinking problem, that most of her other problems stemmed from that. She agreed to go.

She was fascinated by the people she met at this particular meeting. They were very kind, rather witty, and certainly to Sheila's very confused mind, well brought up and upper class. She thought A.A. was marvelous —but not for her. She could not accept the fact that she was an alcoholic. She had never been to a doctor, had never been in any real trouble, had had no car accidents, nor lost anything really worth while. She was, however, a completely different personality than she had been. She was confused, bored, cynical, unfeeling, irresponsible, and terribly afraid of life and the future.

She continued to drink, but she also began to wonder about it. A.A. had at least done that much for her. Her home life was now totally unbearable; she stayed away as much as possible. One day at a luncheon with her A.A. friend, she met a very interesting man, John. He was very attractive, charming, and quite brilliant. He had lost one of the biggest jobs in the television industry through drinking. Yet, even though he could not reach any of his former friends and the industry doors were closed to him, he seemed happy, calm, and optimistic. He was in A.A. He told Sheila she had certainly turned into one of the boys. This was the shock she needed.

She found out later in A.A. that she had reached her "bottom." She also discovered that the days of the Bowery alcoholics are over, that you reach your bottom when you can no longer live with yourself. You then have two choices open to you: You can either get sober or you can become a complete vegetable, end up in an institution, and die.

Sheila found it extremely difficult to admit to herself or to anyone else that she could be an alcoholic. The word was, in her mind, bound up irrevocably with a lack of morality and a lack of will power. She slowly discovered that she had a disease, a killing disease at that. She learned that once she took the first drink she could not stop. That it was the first drink that got her drunk. She learned that the only way to arrest her disease was to stop drinking altogether. She learned to do this, painfully and nervously, one day at a time. At first, she said, it was one hour at a time, then it expanded. Anyone can stay away from a drink for one hour, and eventually that becomes habitual. Sobriety, like alcoholism, is progressive.

Sheila was very lucky; she had never heard of pills. Drinking was sociability and gregariousness to her; taking pills was solitary and defeatist. With the help of

20

John, she started up the road back. She married him and has one of the greatest marriages I have ever seen. It is based on mutual love and understanding, mutual trust, and the profound joy that conquering a problem together can give. They have had much trouble: serious illnesses, three parental deaths, loss of jobs, and legal problems. Sheila's father died an alcoholic in a state institution. She said it was the total waste of a brilliant man; and the waste of life and ability that alcoholism causes is the thing she hates most about it. Sheila's story was and is a simple one: no scandal, no horror, no institutions, no hospitals. It was the downslide of a "Golden Girl"—to as far down as *she* cared to go. A small private tragedy, so easy to accomplish.

If you have any kind of a liquor or pill problem, don't doubt. Don't wait. Don't lie to yourself. Get busy —now. As Sheila said to me, "Tomorrow may be too late."

# III

# The

# Family

ALCOHOLIC influence begins in the home. Many doctors believe that alcoholism in the young is encouraged most through the power of example. Parents who drink too much or, conversely, who don't drink at all *and are adamant about it* tend to produce alcoholic children. Though there are no hard-and-fast rules about what causes the disease, in one case it is the power of example, in the other the spirit of rebellion. You can find many sociological treatises and medical reports in your library on family backgrounds; mores; and religious, ethnic, and cultural influences toward alcoholism. From my own experience and that of friends and acquaintances, I will attempt to describe what some of these influences can mean to you.

In American heterogeneous, mobile, upward-thrusting society, religious and class distinctions become blurred faster than ever before. Alcoholism and pill addiction, great social equalizers, can attack any girl, whether she be wealthy or poor; intellectual or stupid; Jewish, Catholic, or Protestant; upper, middle, or lower class. However, girls from the upper and lower classes tend to drink the most. Girls from the middle class are usually too status-conscious, too concerned with rising socially, or too morally bound in to become involved with liquor.

Girls born on the lowest rung of society, unless they are raging beauties or exceptionally brilliant, feel life is fairly ugly anyhow; they might as well drink.

Girls from the best families are surrounded by the protection that money can give. They often feel they can get away with anything and everything; and they can for a while. Money *can* buy good doctors; ways out of drunken-driving accidents; months at health spas, beauty farms, and private sanitariums. These girls often find it much more difficult to sober up than others. They have no reason to do so, except one: They get sick and tired of being sick and tired.

I will give you a composite picture of a young girl almost certainly headed for alcohol or pill addiction:

> She is given a "training" bra at eight.
> She knows all about sex at ten.
> She is encouraged to "date" at twelve.
> She must make the "right" dances with the "right" boys.
> She must get into the "right" school.
> Mother is always pushing, nagging, cajoling, encouraging her daughter to be what *she* was not.
> She is given too much of the wrong kind of freedom.

Daddy is never there. Daddy makes the money, sometimes honestly, sometimes not.

Daddy plays golf with his friends, drinks with his cronies, sleeps with his secretary.

She may have a sister who is prettier or more talented.

If she is twenty and not married or engaged, she is a failure.

Or, in some cases, she is encouraged to stay at home and take care of Mommy or Daddy, to have no life of her own.

If this, in any way, sounds like you or your daughter, beware!

Joan was the daughter of one of the most famous and wealthy families in the United States. She fled from her Eastern, progressive college in her junior year to elope with an equally immature but social Ivy Leaguer. Life was gay; life was charming. Joan and her husband led a completely F. Scott Fitzgerald existence across two continents. Eventually the marriage began to pall, especially after the birth of a child. Joan got a divorce, relinquished custody of her child to her husband, and struck out on her own.

She became the gay and gilded darling of the Eastern seaboard. She began to drink, not wisely and not well. She was very soon a full-blown alcoholic with few emotional resources to fall back on. Although her family contributed money, they gave her little else. She was soon too ashamed to see them and wound up drinking suicidally in a cheap hotel near the "Bowery" of a big city. An old friend of hers, a member of Alcoholics Anonymous, finally found her, easily spotted her problem, and recommended A.A. After hospitalization, Joan joined Alcoholics Anonymous and finally "made the program."

She then got a good but very demanding job. Someone in her office told her about pills. Joan discovered that if she took one phenobarbitol it would help her sleep at night. If she took one in the morning it would help her through her grueling day. Forgetting her alcohol addiction, she was soon taking barbiturates regularly —to sleep, to wake up, to keep going. One day, walking down a main street in her town, she went completely out of her mind. She wound up in a straight-jacket in the psychiatric ward of the city hospital.

After more hospitalization, she fought her way out of the pill problem. However, as she moved once again up the scale of success in business, life got rough. Dangerously, she thought once more of pills and began taking them again, thinking one at a time would do little or no harm. But for an addict, since there is no such thing as one, she was soon on the carousel once more. This time she went "insane" on a cross-country trip. She was met at the nearest town by doctors and nurses with the now familiar straight-jacket. At present she is still on pills and has reverted to drinking. She is barely functioning. Will she come out of it again? She hasn't yet; it remains to be seen.

If you have an alcoholic mother, you know what tragedy is. If you are an alcoholic mother get help right now. Your illness will cause neurosis and mental troubles for your children and your children's children!

If you wonder or even suspect that your mother's strange behavior is the result of alcohol, but you are

not certain, let me point out a few obvious signs for
you.

>She may get drunk at her own parties or, at the
least, have a few drinks before the party begins.

>She may next hide bottles, in the bathroom hamper,
under the mattress, in the kitchen cupboard, anywhere at all.

>She may add water to your family liquor supply, to
cover for the liquor she has been sneaking out of
the bottles.

>She may embarrass you in front of your friends; she
will probably always drink at the wrong time.

Next come visits to the doctor, "sick" headaches,
darkened rooms, hospitals—sanitariums. If you are rich
enough, your mother goes away frequently—to spas,
resorts, beauty farms, drying out places. If you are
poor, the social worker is a frequent visitor at your
house.

Try to understand your mother. She does not want to
be the way she is. Above all, do not drink along with
her. That is certainly not the way to help her—or yourself. Remember, alcoholism is not physically hereditary,
but the environment that fosters it is insidious. You may
sympathize with your mother, or you may be agonized
and ashamed of her behavior. You may fling yourself
into a bad marriage, or run with very bad company to
escape. But you cannot run from yourself.

Screaming at, berating, your mother won't help. Nor
will pouring her liquor down the drain, hiding her bottles, or cutting off her credit at the liquor store. An
alcoholic can and will always obtain liquor in some
form: vanilla, mouthwash, cough syrup—perfume if

27

necessary. Or she will hoard tranquilizers and barbiturates against the day the liquor runs out.

The ONLY way your mother will stop drinking is if she herself wants to stop. She cannot do it for you or for your father, but only for herself. If you can help her to help herself, that's your answer. Do not gossip or complain about your mother; she has her own private hell. And she wouldn't gossip about you!

If, though, you have an alcoholic father, you share your problem with literally millions of girls in America. Many, many men live lives of semi-alcoholic stupor. They may be daily drinkers: at lunch, after work, on the commuter train, at home, at the country club, at parties, especially on weekends. They may be periodic or binge drinkers, sober most of the time but likely to disappear on a long drunk without warning. Some men never cross that invisible line into alcoholism; they remain very heavy drinkers all their lives. But alcohol still colors their personalities, their attitudes, and their relationship with you. No man or woman is truly himself, if he is full of alcohol or pills. Still other fathers cross over sometime in their drinking careers and become unemployed, irresponsible, unemployable "neighborhood drunks."

One of the worst things your father's alcoholism can do to you is to sour you on men. All men are not alcoholics; all men are not rotten, nor are they oversexed, homosexual, or childish. Many men are just plain wonderful. If you keep your psyche straight, you'll probably find one.

If your friends taunt you about your father's drinking, do your best to ignore them. It's not easy, but it can be done. Don't bring them home—ever! You will never know your father's condition before you arrive. If there is no money, because he has spent it all on liquor, try to keep up your appearance anyhow. Keep yourself as neat, clean, and as well-dressed as possible. You can work after school. If you are already working, do not, under any circumstances, give your father money. He will only drink with it, and perhaps encourage you to drink along with him. If your father is belligerent when drinking, stay away from home when you know he is in that condition. Try to remove yourself intellectually and emotionally, if you cannot do so physically. Find and attend the Ala-Non or Ala-Teen meetings of Alcoholic Anonymous in your town or city. There you will find solace, help, and friends who share your problem. Ala-Non is a group of friends and relatives of still-drinking or arrested alcoholics who meet to discuss their mutual problems. They learn through understanding and mutual help how to cope with "their" alcoholic, and also how to work on their own problems, which may have contributed to this alcoholism. Ala-Teen is a similar group for the teenage sons and daughters of alcoholics.

Do not ride in a car your father is driving. Do your level best to keep him from driving even if he has consumed only a small amount of liquor. Safety experts believe that over half of the fifty thousand vehicular deaths in America in 1965 were caused by pathologically drunken drivers. Never drive, yourself, for a lark if you have had anything to drink.

Read as much as you can about alcoholism so you'll be informed; in fact, read as much as you can about everything. Books are great companions, and they don't cause trouble.

If you suspect your father is becoming alcoholic, try

29

to talk to him about it—quietly, when he is not drunk. A Saturday or Sunday morning when he has a hangover is usually a good time. He may talk to you when he will not talk to your mother. Don't get fighting mad; don't upbraid him. Anything you can say, he has said to himself a thousand times already. Recommend that he see his doctor or talk to someone in A.A. That is all you can do.

If you are unsuccessful in helping him, and the problem grows worse, talk to your minister, priest, or school counselor. Or go to the family doctor yourself. If you and your mother must move out, do so—without delay. This is often the shock your father needs to help him sober up. Worrying, cajoling, pleading, nagging, and threatening are useless. He will only drink more to hide from your words. Encourage your father to do something for himself; it is a beginning.

You will undoubtedly build resentments against your father. Don't waste your time; they will do you no good whatsoever. Learn one thing now: resentment *never* bothers the other person; it only destroys you. Try to pull down the curtain in your own mind; keep busy. If the problems are overwhelming, call your local community service or the National Council on Alcoholism. Don't wish your father dead a thousand times a day. He is already dead.

Alcoholic parents can ruin your life only if you let them. It will help to know you share this particular problem with millions of other girls. Above all, do not follow parental example. It will be very easy to do so. You will feel very sorry for yourself; you will feel life has short-changed you. But you will only become another mistake in the book of life if you drink. If you are headed that way now, stop at once and get help.

If you live at home and it is ghastly, move out. A cheap apartment alone or with a roommate, in peace, is preferable to the most elegant mansion full of drunks or "pill babies." You can do it. Others have done it before you; many more will after you. There is hardly a family in this nation that does not have an alcoholic somewhere in its family tree.

If you have younger children in your care, do your best for them. If your parents' alcoholism has progressed to a great extent, have them committed to an alcoholic hospital. You can get them in free, if you must. Drastic? Perhaps. But it is survival—theirs and yours. And survival under the poorest conditions is preferable for all of you to death at home. Death it will be, without help.

Try not to be bitter; try not to let your parents' alcoholism color your whole life. Remember: the choice is yours.

# IV

# How to Tell

# If You Are Alcoholic

A MAN once asked J. P. Morgan how much it cost to run his yacht. Morgan replied: "Nobody who has to ask what a yacht costs has any business owning one." That's the way it is with alcoholism. If you are asking, if you are worried, the chances of your having the disease are very good.

There is no such thing as being just a little bit alcoholic. Like a pregnancy, it develops. It cannot get better if you continue to drink. It will get worse much faster if you add pills to your liquor problem.

The choice is yours, yours alone. You cannot be forced into sobriety. Either you stop drinking, stop lying to yourself about your problem, or you destroy yourself. Your choice, very simply, is sobriety or the grave.

These are the early stages and symptoms of alcoholism:

Great fondness for drinking.

Not eating with people who don't drink; not eating at all.

Preoccupied with drinking; thinking about it constantly.

Looking forward to parties and gatherings where there will be a great deal of liquor.

Not going to parties where there won't be liquor.

Feeling you cannot function without alcohol; drinking before parties where liquor will be served.

Getting "high" often, even on a small amount of alcohol. Quantity has *nothing* to do with it; it depends on what you need and use alcohol for.

Lying about getting "high."

Not having hangovers, or saying you don't.

Making sure there is always a supply of liquor in the house.

Sneaking drinks.

Watering the liquor when you have sneaked drinks.

Lying to yourself about how much you are drinking. A normal drinker doesn't have to lie.

"Needing" a drink at a certain time every day.

Drinking when you shouldn't—before a big meeting or an important dinner—when you come home alone, especially after having had a great deal to drink already.

Looking forward to drinking alone.

Drinking to go to sleep.

Not caring about how you look. Or, conversely, becoming overconscious of how you look.

Not getting close to people so that you don't breathe in their faces.

Lying to your husband about anything, but especially about your drinking.

Lying to your parents or employers.

Slacking on your work.

Foggy thinking.

Spending too much money, and not caring.

Personality change when drinking—withdrawal or belligerency.

Being defensive about your drinking.

RED ALERT: Drinking, for any reason, in the morning. If you sleep in the morning, and your morning is 3 P.M., drinking then.

There is an intermediate stage, which has its symptoms, too.

Getting fat and jowly-looking.

Nightmares and not sleeping, except when passed out.

Passing out.

Complete loss of efficiency at job, home, school, everywhere.

Inability to discern the truth.

Enormous guilt feelings about everything.

Not caring about anything.

Blackouts. If you've reached this stage and are still drinking, you are in real trouble.

Feeling sorry for yourself constantly.

Resenting everyone else.

Very, very low frustration point.

Hating yourself.

Neglecting your teeth.

Taking pills.

Loss of jobs.

Your husband leaving you, or threatening to do so.

Your children avoiding you.

Loss of physical control.

Parents panicky.

Jealousy.

Running from doctor to doctor, lying to them all.

Drunk on weekends—or every night.

Throwing money around.

Doing anything to get a drink.

Waking up in strange beds.

Thinking of nothing else but drinking.

Suicidal thoughts.

The shakes.

Total feeling of hopelessness and worthlessness.

Lack of any concern about family, religion, morality, ethics, honor.

Guilt, guilt, guilt!

There are also the late stages otherwise known as: why didn't I do something about this before now!

Nothing concerns you but alcohol; you'll do anything to have a drink.

You see physical symptoms of disease about which you do nothing.

Fogged, confused all the time.

Drinking cheaper and cheaper types of alcohol—cheap wine, vanilla extract, canned heat.

Taking much less alcohol to get drunk.

Visits to hospitals, sanitariums, institutions.

Delirium tremens.

Death.

The symptoms of addiction to pills are practically the same—general malaise, disorientation, removal from reality and so on. The results are the same, too—institutions and death.

# V

# Your

# Looks

GIRLS and women often have very little edge with which to sell themselves to the outside world except their looks and their personalities. If they are alcoholics, these are the first things to go!

An alcoholic woman, unless she locks herself in a sealed room, cannot hide what alcohol is doing to her. The ravages of alcohol are far worse than the ravages of time. It can turn a twenty-year-old into a forty-year-old, a forty-year-old into an old woman. And it doesn't take long.

You may first notice that you are drinking too much when you look into your mirror—if you look into it honestly, which is very difficult. Your skin will begin to look coarse; it will have a rough, uncared for texture. It often will become quite ruddy, or a sick yellow-gray. You are not eating correctly; your skin, the largest organ in your body, is not properly nourished.

You may be leaving your makeup on at night, because you are often too drunk to remove it. Soon you will give up makeup altogether. It is impossible to apply eyeliner with a hangover. Have you ever tried putting on mascara when you have the shakes? The pores in your skin will enlarge; your whole face will look as if it had slipped a little. You will look "blurred." Soon you will develop some kind of skin disease, which will not be curable by ointments, salves, or pills. Strange rashes, odd blemishes, unexpected coloration, gray patches, peeling and scaling, and other phenomena will appear. Your nails will split, peel, and break.

If you are a pill addict, your skin will become sluggish; tranquilizers slow down circulation. Your skin will take on a sallow, muddy color. It will look dead. Your eyes will look dead; strange things happen to the pupils. Your hair will be lifeless; your hand movements slow. You will often be quite unco-ordinated; you will not remember how to walk.

Your speech will become blurred and repetitive. On pep pills your movements will become jerky and compulsive. You will sound loud and garrulous. You will not remember what you have said five minutes before.

The action of pills on your appearance is different from that of alcohol, but the result is the same. Neither will leave you the desirable, lovely, charming woman you want to be.

If you drink compulsively, something happens to your hair. Since you are too busy drinking, you will not wash it often. It becomes lank, stringy, dirty, and unkempt. If you affect a style requiring combs and hairpins, they will fall out. You may resort to cutting it off in a "butch" cut. It will look plastered to your skull. You may try to hide it under a hat or scarf, neither of which is clean. Your hair smells; you begin to smell.

There is a certain odor exuded by alcoholics; it comes right through the pores of your body. It is unmistakable; if there is enough alcohol in your system, showers or baths will not wash it away. It pervades your clothes; you cannot get it out. When you open your closet door, it will overpower you. You do not have your clothes cleaned. General cleanliness disappears rapidly. You will not bathe or shower often enough. You fear falling in the tub. Conversely, during sober bouts, guilt-ridden, you will bathe maniacally. You think you can bathe away the shame, guilt, and remorse. You cannot.

Weight is the deadliest give-away of all. If you tend to obesity, you will get fat very fast when you drink. All alcohol is laden with calories. In the beginning you may eat; but that will soon stop and you will only drink. You will still gain weight, if your body is geared that way. There is a certain look to the flesh of a woman drinker. She usually gets very bloated around the chin line. There is a puffiness there that is not from food, a white flab that looks like the underbelly of a flounder. Your eyes will become slitty, raw, and red-looking. They will puff underneath. There is no concealing this look; all the white makeup in the world will not hide nor blot out the poached-egg eyes of the drinker.

Of course, your figure will go. Midriff bulge becomes midriff bloat. Your chest and shoulders will sag; your upper arms will look like hams. Your legs will get flabby from lack of exercise. You will look like a swollen gray sack.

If you tend to be thin, though, you will get thinner. You will begin to look emaciated. Your skin will be drawn tight over your cheekbones; you will look like a death's head. What little flesh you have will hang from your bones in loose, crepey folds. Your legs and arms will look like matchsticks, and will be about as useful.

Often, women who drink for a long time have a re-treaded tire-look—a beaten up look, and a beaten look. Some have a very haunted, drawn, ghostly mien. Others a very coarse, puffed up, weather-beaten look. Unless you are young when you stop drinking, you may never be able to erase completely what has happened to your face. At any rate, it will take a long time.

There is a certain walk a woman alcoholic has that is also a dead giveaway. It is like walking on eggs. She places each foot very carefully. Dennis Coffey, the Irish poet, described it as weaving your glass limbs about you as you stagger down the street. You will clutch at banisters when negotiating stairs, if, indeed, you can negotiate them at all. You will begin to avoid subways and buses; taxicabs will become your way of transport.

Your voice will, at first, become throaty. You will lie to yourself and tell yourself it is sexy. It isn't. Then it will become gravelly, often from a combination of liquor and cigarettes. You now have the famous whiskey voice. You will become loud, strident, and repulsive. You may often break into tears for no good reason. You will become an emotional, childish misfit. Or your choice of words may deteriorate. Four-letter words you would never use sober will become part of your vocabulary. You may become tough, hard, and shrewish. Everything you say will reflect what you have become: a drunken mess.

You can start to worry about your drinking when you look in your clothes closet and see unpolished shoes with rundown heels; dirty, stained dresses with pins in the hems; coats with linings ripped and buttons missing; handbags that won't close and with the handles ripped off; gloves with holes in the fingers; sweaters grimy and grubby with pulled threads. Your lingerie drawer is a jumbled mess; there are runs in all your stockings. The white nylon is gray. The slips and bras and girdles are ripped, pinned and filthy. You will not spend money on your clothes because that money will go to buy alcohol. Soon you will be unable to shop in the stores at all, or go to the tailor, cleaner, or shoemaker. You'll be too ashamed. Soon, indeed, you will be unable to go anywhere at all.

Here is what will happen to your health. In the beginning nothing ghastly will occur. You will merely become a bit fatter or a bit thinner. But that is only the beginning. Soon, you will cut down on your food intake; then you will give food up altogether. Many women who say they don't eat enough to keep a bird alive, yet keep getting fatter, are secret drinkers. Food spoils the "wonderful" effects of liquor.

Also, there is nothing more nauseating than a good, hearty meal when you have a hangover. Alcoholics, like pregnant women, develop strange tastes in food—cravings for chili at 2 A.M., a love for pickles and other highly spiced foods. In reality, it is all they can taste. Other alcoholics kid themselves by drinking milk or eating ice cream before a drinking bout. It doesn't work. Nothing works if you are alcoholic.

You will become deficient in most vitamins, but especially vitamin B. Liquor and coffee destroy the vitamin B in your system; you will not try to replace it. You will begin to suffer the effects of malnutrition. It will show most of all in your appearance.

You will begin to be sick in the morning. Alcohol is

not a stimulant but a depressant. When its effects begin to wear off, your nerves will be screaming. You will not be able to get the alcohol out of your system with black coffee, steam baths, massages, vitamin pills, or food. Alcohol is absorbed into your bloodstream and is carried to all the organs, tissues and fluids of your body. Your liver oxidizes it and breaks it down. It takes about four hours to oxidize four ounces of alcohol. When your liver becomes overworked, it too will break down. You will develop cirrhosis, edema, and many other problems. The only thing that will get alcohol out of your system is time. If you drink a lot, you will suffer a lot. You will then take more liquor to ease the suffering. Your system will never really be free from it. Alcoholics Anonymous says it takes at least three months to remove all traces of alcohol from the system.

Your heart will begin to pound at odd times, especially if you are a brandy drinker. The palms of your hands at the lower outside corners will turn a strange pink color; it is a sign your liver is starting to malfunction. You will have a bloated stomach, a continuous driving thirst, strange kinds of pruritus and a general inability to function. These are all symptoms of a problem growing worse.

If you smoke, you will suffer from burns on your person and on your clothes. You may burn yourself to death by falling asleep while smoking in bed. Many, many alcoholic women have died this way. Don't say to yourself you never smoke in bed. When you are drunk, you don't know whether you do or not.

You will suffer from sprained ankles on a fairly regular basis. Cuts and bruises are normal, so are black eyes. You will keep falling over things, into things, and down things. You may turn on the gas and not remember doing it. If you light a match, you may never remember anything again. If you drive while drinking, or while you are taking pills in increasing quantities, you will have an enforced sobriety—in the hospital. Or in the morgue.

Briefly, in the early stages of alcoholism and pill addiction, your health will begin to deteriorate in many ways. Your nerves will be in terrible shape. Depression will become a way of life. Your appearance, the façade you present to the world outside, will become slovenly, sloppy, unkempt and, finally, revolting. You—the pretty, charming, bright American woman—will fall hard and fast. The higher you are, the lower you fall. And you're doing it all yourself!

# VI

# Your

# Job

TODAY, work is where the action is. Many girls first learn to drink on the job. Dr. Marvin Block, chairman of the American Medical Association Committee on Alcoholism, says women are alcoholic in a ratio of men one to one. Reports of a three-to-one ratio in favor of men stem from families shielding women more than they do men from the stigma of "alcoholism." Dr. Robert Garber of the Carrier Clinic, New Jersey, feels women's problems in this respect are coming more into the open as they *enter the business world.*

Many doctors feel that alcoholics are neurotic to begin with, and drinking is merely the form their neuroses take. If this is true, a job can be pure heaven, especially when you are young. It is often your first feeling of freedom, of the power that comes from earning your own money. You are either going to set the business world on fire or you are going to mark time until you get married. And the office is a great hunting ground for men. If you are married and have children, the office represents cars, clothes, dinners, mortgage payments, and trips you ordinarily would not have on one salary. In short, the office is all things to all girls, including the start of a lot of trouble.

If you are bright and well-educated, the first sign of trouble may be boredom. You feel you are geared for bigger and better things than you are doing. You begin to loathe the details and the routine. You feel your boss is not as capable or as bright as you are. If you hold the seeds of alcoholism within you, you want the biggest and best job right away. You cannot and will not wait. Your future will begin to seem a little dim.

You will start to drink at lunch with your friends. Or you will start to drink at lunch with men higher up on the office social scale, figuring it's one way to get there yourself. Soon, you will meet them for drinks after work; it's much more fun to go to a cozy bar than to go home to mother, roommate, or dull husband. The after-work cocktail hour will get longer and longer, so will your lunch hour. You will give up shopping at lunchtime. It's much more pleasant to sit and drink with the girls and boys. You may start with sherry, but you will wind up with martinis. You will discover they give you the fastest "jolt" for your money. You will gradually stop drinking diluted drinks like scotch and water.

Or your problem may not be boredom. It may be pressure. This is indigenous to the TV industry, to advertising, fashion, publishing, cosmetics, newspaper and magazine work, and to allied creative fields. Your hours may be erratic; you may work from 7 A.M. to midnight. You will gulp your food where you find it. You become nervous; your job is always on the line. You can't sleep.

48

If you are struggling and ambitious, you may have lied a bit to get your job. And now you have to deliver. You are in over your head.

You will start drinking to keep going. You feel the cocktail hour is the only way to entertain clients—and to entertain account men, buyers, editors, designers, and all the other men, women, and homosexuals you find so fascinating. The more you drink, the more fascinating they will become. You feel scared all the time, but you can't get out; you like the things your large salary is buying for you. If you are married, chances are you and your husband are mortgaged to the hilt. You feel you must live in Greenwich or Grosse Point or Beverly Hills; you must live like the Chairman of the Board. It is the American way. You need your job—badly. So you begin to drink more and more. You will start to take pills to wake up in the morning, and pills to put you to sleep at night. You are on the treadmill; the rat race has you by the throat.

Soon you are not quite sober most of the time. And people are beginning to notice. Don't believe for one minute that they aren't. PEOPLE KNOW! You never, never get away with being alcoholic. If you are a book-keeper or cashier, mistakes will show up early. If you are a sales girl, you will insult customers, lose sales. If you are a secretary, you cannot type without lots of mistakes. If you are a teacher, you miss school. If you are the woman's page editor of a newspaper, you will delegate authority to your assistant. You think you can relax. You can; she will soon have your job.

In a world of harsh competition, where women are not exactly welcomed, Susan was a shining star. She had started her career as a secretary, became a copywriter for a big retail chain, and eventually a cub reporter on a newspaper. She was brilliant. She worked her way up to being women's page editor of one of the largest papers in the country.

Along with her work, she learned a few other things. She learned how to write and how to compete with men; she also learned how to drink like a man. She made her money like a man; why shouldn't she enjoy a man's privileges. Every five o'clock would find her at the bar of a famous newspaper hangout tossing off her martinis. She was usually still there at midnight. Because she was so bright, she could still write and produce better than two other women. Eventually, she fell in love with an editor of the paper. He was married, but trying to get a divorce. He was also alcoholic. While they waited together for his divorce, they drank together. Soon Susan was to be seen early in the morning in her favorite bar pouring an eye-opener down her throat— to get going, to get the column out. She was "blessed" at this time with a super-able secretary, a young girl with talent and ambition. More and more, Susan tossed her responsibilities and her job in the lap of her secretary. The secretary was good at both of them.

Eventually, of course, Susan was fired, as was the editor to whom she was now married. Together, they took the "geographical" cure—drinking their way across the country and back. They could no longer hold regular jobs; but they eked out a living with free-lance assignments, plus money from family and friends. They wound up in a cold-water flat drinking around the clock. Susan died; her husband, not unusually, sobered up and then married again.

Susan's secretary is today one of the most famous and respected fashion writers and arbiters in the world.

She always had the talent; her opportunity was provided by Susan's alcoholism.

Even if you decide not to drink directly on the job, you will drink at office parties and little gatherings. You may pass out in the TV studio or at the fashion showing. You will, sooner or later, make a fool of yourself. If you drink uptown, downtown, anywhere away from your place of business, someone who shouldn't will see you.

An alcoholic cannot hide! Very often, you will be proud of your drinking prowess; you will display it. You will soon become "one of the boys," always good for a laugh. If you are a writer or an artist, or someone vaguely creative, you feel you need liquor to spark the muse. How unfortunate. The best books, ads, columns, and jobs are written and done by sober, concentrating women, who are fully on the job twenty-four hours a day. In spite of what you may read, the business world is still a man's world. It is difficult enough to succeed as a sober, intelligent, charming woman. It is impossible as an alcoholic.

You will soon be hiding a bottle in your desk drawer. You will tell yourself it's great fun, very F. Scott Fitzgerald. Your lunch hours will begin at eleven, or even earlier. They will run to two or three in the afternoon. On your way to work in the morning, your orange or tomato juice will have a shot of vodka in it. You think people cannot smell vodka. You will drink all night, every night, into the wee hours of the morning. Or you will sober up and not drink at all during the week, going on binges on weekends. You will begin to miss Mondays at work on a fairly regular basis. The days after holidays will not find you on the job. You are now

51

never really sober. The next step is inevitable: you will be fired!

If you have been with your firm or school or hospital for years, they may take pity on you. They may send you to the company doctor, to a hospital, or even a sanitarium. They may just gently warn you. This is becoming rarer. Big companies may have an alcoholic program; they may be enlightened; they may try to help. But it is extremely difficult for a boss or a personnel director to tell a woman she is an alcoholic. And they cannot afford mistakes like you.

Soon, perhaps, your boss will call you in and explain they are having a budget cut. Or they are losing the account—with your actions in the past, this is entirely possible. Or they are changing the department, consolidating, moving—or something. Your services are no longer required. Your boss will probably be very embarrassed and quite kind about this. Too bad. If more bosses called a spade a spade earlier, more alcoholics would seek help sooner. Women often tend to seek help when they are exposed. If your boss is foul to you about your drinking, be grateful. He's doing you a favor.

You are now thoroughly sorry for yourself. No one understands you. You may hide out for a time and drink yourself into a stupor. They may have given you good severance pay. You will not buy food nor pay the rent with it. You will drink.

Or you, scared and trying to fight back, may immediately go and look for another job. This is the worst thing you can do! You look dreadful; you will not be able to function properly; and you will be so thoroughly involved with yourself that you cannot possibly do a good job for anyone else! But, strangely enough, because you are alcoholic, you may also from past experience be a superb liar. You will get another job, often a better one. Alcoholics usually do—in the beginning. But you will be fired from this one, too. Sooner. The new firm feels no loyalty to you. You are on the skids.

By now, your reputation is destroyed. You are a risk, an insurance risk, a job risk. And everyone knows! The business world is very small. You, who thought you could handle anything and everything, are finished. If you must work to live you will now take any job—dishwasher, maid, clerk, anything. Anything that will keep that liquor flowing.

You may now decide to change your environment, blaming your drinking on that. You take what is known to alcoholics as the geographical cure—another city, another state, another country. It will not work; you will take yourself and your habit with you. You will only be more alone, with no friends and no family. You will always drink at the wrong time: on business trips, before meetings, and so on. You will not know nor care where you wind up, or with whom. You are now a well-known lush, unemployed, unemployable. It will take you years to come back. If you are just starting, read this and beware. Don't drink where or while you work!

# VII

# Men

You will often start to drink for a man.

If you are young, you may be scared, immature, lacking in social grace and poise. You desire above all else to be popular, beautiful, and loved. You may have had your first drink with your father. You will like what it does for you. You will feel grown-up and charming. Beware! Your father's drinking may have a profound effect on you, whether or not he is alcoholic. Just as daughters of neurotics tend to marry neurotics, daughters of alcoholics tend to marry alcoholics! Having had a drink at home, you feel free and safe to drink when you go out to parties or on your first date. Perhaps your mother disapproves of alcohol in any form. You may drink to spite her. You will drink for a dare. But, secretly, you will drink because alcohol seems to make you into what you think you want to be. Drinking has a mystique about it; you feel it will give you something you don't have. You will drink to be popular, because the other people drink; you will drink for courage, because you feel you are unworthy, unattractive, and unpopular. You will soon have a problem.

Perhaps you are older, and new at school or new in town. You don't know anyone. You are lonely. You will drink with the boys from the office. Or just to find human companionship, you will go to the neighborhood saloon. There, you will always find a male friend willing to drink with you—especially if *you* pay for the drinks. Soon it will become "your" place. The men think you are great fun. You can take it from there.

Because you lack self-confidence, because you don't know who you are, liquor becomes your friend. It becomes the substitute for your weight-reducing program, for visiting the beauty salon and the department store, in short, for making yourself over into what you would like to be and what the boys would really like, too. Liquor loosens your tongue; you see yourself as the witty, charming, beautiful creature you always hoped to be. Men see you as the loud, sloppy, bloated dame they don't care to be seen with. With alcohol or with pills, you will soon lose your inhibitions. You will issue invitations to bed and board, sometimes to veritable strangers. You will do anything to attract and hold a man. You think he wants you to drink with him. You do, and he leaves you. Men can drink with the boys anytime; they don't have to drink with you.

Or perhaps you are truly one of the lucky ones. You are a great raving, tearing beauty. Perhaps you are a model or an actress. You make money; you always have men hanging around. They are not usually the kind who will marry you.

You are trying for a brilliant match, or you are trying

for the top in your chosen field. The competition is very rough. You begin to sleep with producers, with buyers, with vice-presidents. You are caught in the social whirl. You must make the scene; you are out every night in the "right" places. You cannot keep it up without drinking or taking pills. Soon your looks begin to go, and your conscience hurts you. You drink more; you take more pills. You don't know with whom you were out the night before; you may not even recognize him when you roll over in bed in the morning. This happens more often than you think. If it happens to you, even once, get help. There is no way out for you now without outside help.

One of the most beautiful girls I ever knew, Alix, was also one of the most tragic. She was the daughter of an extremely ambitious mother, whose main object in life was to marry her daughter off to someone immensely rich. Alix received the proper education at much sacrifice on her far-from-wealthy mother's part. She became a model, one of the best, most famous, and long-enduring in the ever-changing fashion world.

Alix was seen at all the right places: Long Island, Palm Beach, Newport. She made all the fashionable European watering places in the right seasons, with the right clothes. She was always draped on the arm of a famous and rich man. At one time or other she was reported engaged to a Long Island playboy, the son of a famous politician, a world-renowned dress designer, and an Iranian prince.

She still worked at modeling, but her clothes and jewels and fast cars did not come from her earnings. Her salary went to her mother. To keep up the pace, Alix began to drink. To avoid the hangovers and the "uglies" of her drinking, she also had prescriptions from her Swiss doctor for all kinds of pills. Alix told me once she hated herself. She was an innately decent girl, who had been thrust out into the world to grab as much as she could, as fast as she could. Eventually, after headline escapades with the playboy here and abroad, she married the prince—much to everyone's surprise. Alix never enjoyed one minute of her marriage. She was either drunk or on pills for its duration.

When she was photographed in the ateliers of Paris, she was always glassy-eyed. Her looks were beginning to go; the prince divorced her for adultery. She never really knew what she was doing. She had the money, the homes, the yachts, the clothes, the jewels.

Two years ago Alix took an overdose of sleeping pills; the doctors did not believe it was intentional. She had been drinking so much in her French chateau, where she lived alone, that they did not think she knew how many pills she had taken. She was buried in France, this beautiful American girl. She was twenty-six. Her mother, well taken care of now, has visited her grave each year.

You may be afraid of men. They really terrify you; maybe you don't even realize it. If and when you meet a real man, you are afraid of sex. You begin to drink for courage. You feel you can blot out your fears and heighten your desires with alcohol. Perhaps you will be able to, in the very beginning. But no man wants to make love to a sodden lump or to a girl so high on pills she isn't even there. If you need liquor and pills to be a real woman, go to a doctor.

The more you drink, beyond a certain point, the less sexually interested you become. Liquor will destroy desire as effectively as a fear of pregnancy will. If you drink a lot you may find yourself pregnant. You will not remember to take precautions. If you really believe the way to attract and hold a man is through alcohol you are deluded. It is the fastest way to lose him.

If you are married, your husband will rapidly begin to lose interest in you. If you drink, your behavior will be erratic, nervous, unstable. You will lie to your husband frequently. You may possibly wind up with the milkman, the golf pro, your boss, or your neighbor's husband. Your husband will find out. And he will not stay with you.

For every ten wives who remain with an alcoholic husband, one husband remains with an alcoholic wife. Perhaps a woman feels she must see it through, or she cannot find another man, or she cannot support herself. A man has no such fears.

There is always another woman waiting to take your man. Even if he is seventy and dependent on social security, to a woman who is without, he looks good. Your husband may have driven you to alcoholism in the first place, you feel. First, that is not true; second, it makes no difference. As you become drunker and drunker he will become more and more absent. In the beginning it may be his job that holds his interest. Sooner or later it will be another woman.

You just might be one of those rare women married to a real man. If you are, and your husband is worried about your drinking or nervous about the pills you are taking, listen to him. Go to your doctor before it is too late. The agony of withdrawal is far easier to face than the agony of night after night alone after your great dependence on him. And that's where you will be— alone. Because the greatest man on earth cannot hang around a drunk forever. He may be forced to leave you for the children's sake or for his own survival. He may feel it is the way to make you sober up. It often is. But he will be gone just the same; and you will probably have trouble getting him back. Even if he does return to the house, it will never be the same. He will always wonder. Quit while you're ahead.

If you are still single and drinking heavily, your choice of men will grow more limited. You will not be seeing the nicest men, the gentlemen. You will be hanging around anyone in pants that will drink with you, men you normally don't see socially, boys too young for you, casual acquaintances, men you hardly recognize—anyone or anything at all. You may be robbed; in fact, it is probable. You may very well wind up with your throat cut, because you don't know the man you will pick up, or where. In your few lucid moments, if you take a good look at yourself, you will despise so much what you see that the only man you want to meet will be the liquor delivery boy. You may wind up living with another alcoholic, a man in the same condition as you are. You may become a prostitute to pay for your alcohol. You won't even be very good at that.

You are now at the stage where no man cares. You are a burden to your husband, if you are married and still have one; you are a burden to your boss, if by any chance, you still have a job; you even bug the neighborhood bartender, who is sick and tired of seeing you come in his door to throw up, fall on the floor, or make a scene. You may be suicidal. Put yourself in the hands of a sympathetic doctor or call A.A. Go to your nearest alcoholic hospital or psychiatric outpatient clinic and beg for help. If you make the effort, people *will* help. But you must do it yourself, *for yourself*. You cannot do it for anyone else, not even for the man in your life. Remember, men hate active alcoholic women.

One other serious mistake you may make is to marry while you are drinking. If the man knows you drink as much as you do and marries you anyhow, he is either alcoholic himself or after your money. If he goes with you for any length of time and doesn't know, he's an idiot and you don't want to marry him. An alcoholic marriage will lead in only one direction—the grave! You will have many way stations before that: marriage counsellors, doctors, hospitals, psychiatrists, social workers, welfare. But the end will be the same, if you continue to drink.

If you feel you or your husband have other mental problems and drinking is only a symptom, stop drinking. Chances are you are wrong; most alcoholics feel they are mentally ill at one time or another. When they sober up, they discover most of their problems, mental and otherwise, were caused by alcohol. However, it is possible. But you still cannot do anything about it while you are drinking actively.

Do not marry while drunk or on pills. You will regret it every day you live, which may not be long. Like driving, men and alcohol do not mix. Together they can kill you.

# VIII

# Pills,

# The Sneaky Disease

YEARS ago, if a man or woman was alcoholic and wanted to stop drinking, he did it cold turkey. Or he went to a hospital or sanitarium. If he didn't wish to stop, but only wanted to rid himself of ghastly hangovers, he merely took a "hair of the dog that bit him," in other words more liquor.

Today, all this has changed. In our great scientific enlightenment we have discovered pills that will cure anything and everything. Sometimes they will even cure things we don't have.

Alcoholics have fallen on pills as the great saviors of alcoholic mankind. Well over half, in fact almost eighty percent, of all alcoholics coming to A.A. or to alcoholic hospitals for help are addicted to pills as well as to alcohol. Alcoholism in and of itself is a very serious disease. Coupled with an addiction to pills, it is often fatal. Pills which alcoholics take to cure their hangovers, to keep them functioning are usually much more difficult to stop taking than the liquor itself. If the alcoholic is addicted to both, his withdrawal problems are terrible. What is not understood by the general public, nor often by the medical profession itself, is that a pill is the same to an alcoholic as a drink. The two are synonymous, inter-changeable, and equally deadly. They are both crutches; they are both withdrawals from reality. They are both very dangerous.

There are many kinds of pills—red, purple, green, blue, white, orange, yellow. There are sleeping pills and sedatives, wake up pills and energy pills, tranquilizers and barbiturates. They go by many names: phenobarbitol, seconal, dexedrine, valium, codeine, meprobomate, ox-anamide, diazepam, benactyzine hydrochloride, diphen-ylmethane, and so on. There are, literally, thousands of names and kinds. Each one has a different effect. Used on and by non-addictive personalities, they have great value. Used by alcoholics, the end result of all of them is the same: addiction, followed by difficult withdrawal or death.

One of the most serious, though often unrecognized, problems confronting this nation is the easy availability of addictive drugs. And make no mistake about it, seda-tives, barbiturates, and tranquilizers are just as much addictive drugs as are heroin, morphine, and cocaine.

Often a girl will try her first pill to relieve a hang-over. She will probably have gotten it from a friend. Or she will go to the doctor and tell him she is nervous, upset, and overwrought. He will write a prescription. He doesn't know she is nervous and upset because she is hung over, unless he is an extremely astute physician who knows her well or is looking for something like this. She finds immediate, blessed relief from her depression, shakes, nausea, and remorse in that little white or purple pill. She has found the answer. Soon, she is taking pills regularly. Her supply runs out. If it is very soon, she cannot go back to the same doctor. So she goes to another one, and he gives her a prescription. She becomes a collector of prescriptions. As an alcoholic, she is a sneak. She knows enough not to go to the same liquor store all the time, so she does not go to the same pharmacy all the time either. She may have a prescription at every drug store in town. Sometimes they are refillable. Sometimes she has known the pharmacist for years, and he will give her a refill. She begins to hoard her little pills, the way she conserved and hoarded her liquor supply against an emergency.

She may go to a psychiatrist for help. He may not believe she is an alcoholic; psychiatrists sometimes do not understand the alcoholic problem. The first thing he may do is to give her a refillable prescription for a little pill to calm her down. She may be a nurse and know where to get pills very easily. She may have connections with a pharmaceutical house, have a doctor in the family, or have a good friend who does. She may travel frequently. It is very easy to get all kinds of pills in Europe. The laws are not as stringent as here. No matter how she does it, once she has sampled the delights of the little pills, she will manage to obtain them. Whether she bootlegs them from student junkies, buys them illicitly on the black market, or just keeps going from doctor to doctor, she will keep her supply of pills intact.

Until very recently the medical profession has sometimes been quite remiss about giving sedatives, tranquilizers, and barbiturates to alcoholics. They cannot be blamed entirely. A doctor has enough to do treating physical illnesses like broken legs, heart trouble, and cancer, without spending hours and hours of his valuable time on what he may feel are neurotic women. If a doctor knows a woman is an alcoholic he often does not have the time to work with her to help her; sometimes he doesn't have this knowledge. He may recommend treatment elsewhere; she may refuse it. The doctor is then forced to the wall. Does he give her a prescription to keep her from jumping out of her skin, or out of a window, or does he get telephone calls at 3 A.M. from an hysterical drunk.

Or, the doctor may not know his patient is an alcoholic. He may never have seen her before, or he may have no reason to suspect she drinks to excess. Again it is not necessarily the doctor's fault.

Carol was a shy, extremely bright young girl when she came out of the Midwest. She had graduated from college and taken her master's degree when she was very young. She met an architect her own age in a big city and married him. After the birth of her second child they moved to a typical, upper middle class, suburban town. Carol joined the usual women's groups, the clubs and so forth. She found to her surprise that she was drinking more than she ever had, and couldn't understand why.

Yet Carol had a strange drinking pattern. Her capacity was very small. She would get "high" on two drinks and "black out" on three or four. Obviously there was something physically wrong with her; a liquor problem never occurred to her. She went to her local doctor and explained her problem. After extensive tests he found nothing wrong physically. He recommended a psychiatrist. Carol entered therapy and talked about her life to the psychiatrist. She drank, she told him, very little. This doctor never suspected alcohol either, nor had he any reason to. But Carol continued her small intake of liquor and began to withdraw more and more from reality. She was no longer able to cope with her life—her husband and her children. Panic-stricken, she entered a private sanitarium. They diagnosed her case as brain disintegration, progressive and probably hopeless.

Carol, after eliminating many other possibilities, reflected in a rare and lucid moment on her drinking and her use of alcohol. She timidly asked the doctors if she might be allergic to alcohol. They scoffed at the idea, remarking that three drinks don't make an alcoholic. In despair, she left the sanitarium and returned home. She continued to drink; she also took sedatives. Again, she began to fall apart at the seams.

One day her minister came to see her to find her in hysterics. She blurted out her whole story to him. She was very lucky; she had a clergyman who knew something about the alcoholic-pill pattern. He suggested she contact her local branch of Alcoholics Anonymous. She did, and went to several meetings. She could not believe this was her problem, however, so she kept on drinking and taking pills. After two more hospitalizations her husband threatened to take the children and leave her for good. She went back to A.A. to try again. This time she met a very attractive woman with the same background and somewhat the same problem she had. This woman worked with Carol very patiently until she stopped drinking and relying on pills. Eventually, Carol's problems cleared up. Sober, she returned to her psychiatrist and continued therapy. Today, she has two more children, a happy marriage, and is studying for her PhD.

Carol was an alcoholic; but because her intake was

so small, no doctor could be blamed for not suspecting alcoholism. It is not *how* much you drink; it's what you use alcohol for.

Often, a doctor will prescribe tranquilizers to help a patient over what he believes to be a nerve-wracking, trying time. Little does he know how nerve-wracking and trying it is to become. Like alcoholism, pill addiction is progressive.

However, as more and more literature is produced, as more and more doctors recognize alcoholism for the disease it is, as more and more people in A.A. tell their stories of alcohol and pill addiction, the problem is coming out into the open. Doctors are now becoming wary. The government is more and more interested in the problem of pill addiction every day. Private sanitariums have become more aware of the situation, too—although some of the less reliable ones still cater to a patient's demands with a pill. No doctor should prescribe sedatives or tranquilizers for any patient unless he is absolutely certain she is a non-addictive personality.

Why pills? What makes them so attractive? Pills are the answer to an alcoholic's prayer. They are the easy way out of pain—psychic and physical. They are easy to carry, easy to take, easy to hide. You cannot smell pills. If you crack up a car, no one can accuse you of drunk driving. If your behavior is erratic and abnormal, no one can smell alcohol on your breath. If you "float" through your days and drug your nights, you are just high-strung. You are not a drunken bum.

But pills are insidious, more insidious than even alcohol. Alcohol at least has the distinction of sometimes being a gregarious way out; it can be convivial, even joyous for a time. Pills never are. Pills are solitary.

Pills are abstract, remote, fearful. You may enjoy alcohol in the company of another; pills you clutch at alone.

What happens when an alcoholic discovers pills? Does she keep on drinking? Usually yes. She merely adds pills to her problems. Eventually the pills become the main problem. With pills, an alcoholic removes herself from reality. She can sleep, wake up and "charge" up, float through the day, never let annoying little problems bother her. Sometimes she takes pills to double or triple the effect of alcohol. Soon, one pill is not enough to do the job. She takes two. From then on, she is dependent, next she is addicted. Pills are a false paradise. Pills promise, but do not deliver.

With pills, you do not care what happens to you, and you don't know that you don't care. A girl can often quit drinking; she finds it incredibly difficult to stop taking pills.

Pills, like alcohol, destroy many things in a woman. Here is a simple parallel:

| BARBITURATE ADDICTION | ALCOHOL ADDICTION |
|---|---|
| *The Beginning* | |
| Tries a pill for the effect. | Drinks to see what effect alcohol will have. |
| Likes it, tries another. | Likes it, drinks another. |
| Begins to lie about how many she is taking. | Lies about her drinking. |
| Uses pills as an escape. | Uses liquor as an escape. |
| *The Middle* | |
| Euphoria, rapidly changing to hostility. | Euphoria, rapidly changing to belligerence, removal from reality, hostility. |
| Depression, tension, nervousness. | Depression, tension, nervousness. |
| Inability to think clearly. | Inability to think clearly. |
| Takes ever-increasing amounts. | Drinks more and more. |

69

*The End*

| | |
|---|---|
| Loss of memory. | Loss of memory, blackouts. |
| Loss of ability to function. | Loss of ability to function. |
| Total lack of care about herself or life. | Total lack of care about anything except another drink. |
| Suicide, inadvertent or intended. | Suicide, inadvertent or intended. |

They destroy her sense of responsibility first. She doesn't care who she is or what is expected of her. She cannot function well—she may for a time, of course, but not for very long. Her memory soon goes. She does not remember what she said yesterday or even two hours ago. She is high, "on a trip," removed. Because she doesn't care about anything, her appearance goes next. Why should she bother? She is beautiful to herself in her own little dream world; why should she make the effort to be beautiful for anyone else. She doesn't know what she is doing at all after a while. A hot stove doesn't feel hot to her. Did she turn on the gas? How did she arrive at the golf club? Did she drive? Safety experts warn that more and more accidents are being caused by drivers who are loaded to the gunwales with pills. They cannot see the lights, except as an onrushing blue glare; they cannot see the white line; they cannot gauge distance and the opposing headlights may be four or four hundred feet away. They maim; they kill; they don't care.

Eventually one of two things happens. A girl will literally go right out of her mind. She may hear Beethoven as she walks down the street; she may walk down the street in the middle of the road. She may begin to see things: nameless, gray-shrouded forms. She may converse at length with someone dead for three hundred years. She is then carted off to the psychiatric ward at the hospital; it is often referred to, unceremoniously, as the flight deck. Or the other thing may happen. She may take an overdose—not deliberately, either. When you are addicted to pills you simply do not know what you are doing. You may think you have taken one sedative; in reality, you may have taken seven. Because even the sturdiest constitutions cannot stand a heavy dosage of barbiturates, tranquilizers, sedatives or a combination of all three, she dies. She did not intend to die; she just died. The heart stopped; the lungs stopped; the organs ceased to function. This can happen very easily, too, if she combines alcohol with pills. It happens every day across the land.

Pills are insidious, sneaky, dirty, and destructive. And you never know. You may think you can estimate how much you can take. You may feel you can drink three scotches and take two seconals. Maybe you can. Tonight. Tomorrow night the three scotches may become four, and your abused and tired system cannot fight anymore. You will be another name on the police "dead on arrival" list. The cause of death may be listed as un-known.

If you are an alcoholic or are becoming one, you are sick. If you add pills to your drinking problem, thinking they will solve it, you are doubly sick. You will be a walking zombie. Your withdrawal will be ghastly, if, indeed, you can withdraw at all. Your strength and reserves will go; you will probably die. This is what the little white or purple pill can do for you.

# IX

# Fear

By now, if you have continued to drink, you are well into the second or middle stages of alcoholism. You probably have added a pill problem to your drinking problem. Your lucid moments, without alcohol and barbiturates, are few. They will grow fewer. You are at the period where you can't stand yourself and you can't stand other people. In your rare, fear-ridden sober moments, the questions you keep asking yourself are: "Where am I going? What is happening to me?"

Strangely enough, because of the nature of this disease and the mystery in which it has been shrouded, you still think you may be able to pull yourself up by your bootstraps without help. Those around you—your parents, husband, children, employers—will insist that you pull yourself together, glue your will power to the sticking point, stop being such a moral coward. You may even say this to yourself, especially if you don't realize you have a disease. Will power is the word you keep repeating to yourself.

But will power means the freedom to choose. It involves the power of choosing and acting according to that choice. If you are an alcoholic, and you take that first drink, you have no choice. You have no choice any more than if you are six months pregnant and you choose not to be. The only choice remaining to you while you continue to drink is what kind of alcohol will you continue to ingest and where.

When you sober up, you will have a choice. You can choose not to take that first drink and learn to live again, or you can choose to take it and die. But this freedom of will comes only when you are sober, not while you continue to drink.

If you have reached this stage of alcoholism, let me remind you again of some of the problems you are facing. Anything and everything reminds you of a drink. You live to drink; you cannot do without it. You desperately need companionship to get away from yourself. If you are single and a normal or reasonably normal girl, you wonder will you ever marry? You will do anything and everything you can to find someone to marry—except stop drinking. You may travel, if you are able. You will go out with anyone who asks you. You will hang around with people you normally wouldn't be caught dead with. You will wind up in strange apartments with strange men. You may move in with one. You will go to bars alone to pick up men. Their color, creed, or station in life will not matter to you. You are now unbelievably desperate for companionship. You will make phone calls in the middle of the night—perhaps to old beaus, who couldn't care less. You will demand to see men you once knew. You will be driven; you will loathe yourself. You will make a fool of yourself no matter what you do. You may make passes at men; you may still be able to kid yourself enough to think they will return them. The reason for all this is very simple: If you are a drinking alcoholic, you do not know what you are doing. You may come home one night and turn on the gas, or walk in front of a bus, or drive your car over a ditch, or take an overdose of sleeping pills. It may not even be intentional, although at this stage of the game it may very well be deliberate.

You may be a different breed. You will probably be living alone by now, because no one can stand to live with you. The loneliness often faced by those who live by themselves will be intensified a thousand times by your alcoholism. Every alcoholic woman I ever knew described herself as terribly, dreadfully lonely. You will stagger in with your bottle of cheap wine. You can no longer afford scotch or rye or even gin. You will proceed to drink yourself into a complete stupor, all night, every night. Your only source of income may be the unemployment bureau; you will just about make it there to sign for your check. This will immediately go for more liquor. You will not eat; you will not spend the money for food, nor will you cook it for yourself. You may keep a cat or a dog for companionship; you will not even feed it. You are by now the most distraught and loneliest of all human creatures, the single woman alcoholic living alone. You have a choice: get to a phone and call for help: A.A., a doctor or a hospital or the police; or kill yourself. There is no other way out.

There are two very sick things you may do. During your slide down into alcoholism, you may have shut men out of your life altogether. You may have discovered you infinitely prefer the company of sympathetic women.

You could be a latent lesbian. Your drinking may unmask your inhibitions about it. You might have a secret fear of being a lesbian, an anxiety, if strong enough that might be a contributing cause to your drinking in the first place. Possible lesbianism may come as a great shock to you; you may not have known or you may have kept it very well-hidden from yourself. But again, because you are an alcoholic, you will not know what you are doing. Your remorse, shame, and guilt in the few sober moments will be indescribable. You will drink more and take more pills to blot out the memory. You are on the sick, sick carousel. You could wind up in a community of abnormal women, wondering how a nice girl like you got there. I'll tell you: you got there by drinking. You can get out by stopping drinking. And going to a psychiatrist.

On the other hand during your drinking career you may have shut men out of your life, but instead of turning to other women, you may have started to run with male homosexuals. It is very easy to do in our society, especially in large urban areas. In the beginning, if you are young, you may not even know that these nice, undemanding men are homosexual.

If you are in a job in a creative field, you may be surrounded by homosexuals. They may be very nice to you; they may flatter you; they may escort you to parties, theaters, dinners when you don't have a date. They may become your very good friends indeed. Many women have a "house" or "token" escort who takes them everywhere. He may be their hairdresser, their decorator, their set designer, their art director. Perfectly acceptable, and no problem. But if you are alcoholic it is part of your fear pattern, your insecurity neurosis that you are not a "real" woman. You feel deep down you cannot attract and hold a "real" man. So you begin to choose homosexuals as a social substitute. Chances are you pay the bills—for the dinners, the liquor, the theater, the trips. You have someone in trousers with you; you can drink as you please. But as you sink deeper and deeper—make no mistake about it—your homosexual companions will desert you; they will gossip and laugh at you behind your back. You have become the bloated figure representing "woman" to them. You prove to them they were right in the first place.

Stop drinking; stop seeing homosexuals. Get sober, get help. Grow up, turn yourself into the woman you were meant to be and find yourself a man. You can only do it when you begin to grow in sobriety.

If you are married, and have reached this step in your alcoholic career without doing something about it, your husband may be about to leave. Or he may already have left. What is there about you to keep your husband? If your husband has a big job or is on his way up, you may have started to drink out of loneliness; he may be away from home much of the time. You regularly made the bar at the country club or the golf club; you may have given gay little cocktail parties on an increasingly regular basis. Soon you may be "stoned" most of the time. The bottles are hidden all over the house. When your husband *does* come home, he usually finds you inebriated. Defiance becomes your coat of armor. Why not, you say. I'll tell you why not. Keep it up and he won't come home at all. Your alcoholism may also have led you down the path to becoming the town tramp. Your looks will be gone. The stories about you will not be kept from your husband's ears. *His* wife is the town drunk, the town lay, the town mess. Unless your husband is a very strong and decent man, he will remove himself very rapidly.

Drinking and alcoholism are the causes of more divorces in suburbia and exurbia than you would believe. The figures on alcoholic suburban housewives are not yet fully known, because these women are often "secret drinkers" or rich enough to be hidden away in sanitariums and health spas. But it is a greatly increasing medical and social problem. The American Dream is fast becoming the American Nightmare because of liquor and pills. Car accidents are on the increase; the divorce rate is rising; alcoholic women live shut up in their own homes. Look around you. How many foggy, unconnected, living-dead women are there in your own neighborhood? Look in your mirror. Are you one?

The ones who suffer most from a married woman's alcoholism are her children. If she is alcoholic, she cannot possibly be a good mother. She may try; God knows she may try. But if she is removed from reality most of the time, how can she succeed? Her children need love; she cannot give it. She does not love herself; how can she love them? She may be divorced; her children don't even have one parent then. She will alternate between periods of great discipline and rigidity, and periods of sloppy affection. She will overcompensate for her drinking and spoil her children. She may hit them indiscriminately while drunk. She may slobber over them when sober or while feeling sorry for herself. She will create scenes in front of their friends until they cannot bring anyone home. Soon they may not come home themselves. She may wreak havoc in their school and with their schoolwork. How can children concentrate on studies, when they don't know if mother loves or hates them that day, or if mother is passed out upstairs every night, or if she comes to their school and raises "Cain" with their teachers.

An older boy may have to be the man of the household; an older girl may have to become a substitute mother. If the father is alcoholic, too, as is often the case, the children have very little chance for emotional survival. Children do not understand that Mommy is sick. To them, she is a drunk, different from their friends' mothers; unreliable, never there when needed, and the cause of many quarrels and much unhappiness. Can you blame children for resenting such a mother? What will they grow up to be? Neurotic, unfeeling, tough, cynical, hard; or weak, perhaps homosexual, emotional babies throughout life, and often alcoholic themselves. Think about this the next time you put your hand on the vodka bottle or pour another scotch down your throat.

Elizabeth came from a poor but reasonably happy family. She was the middle child in a family of six. She was encouraged to marry young, because there was no money for higher education, nor was it to be wasted on a girl. At the age of seventeen, she eloped with a nice boy from the neighborhood who had just scraped through high school. He was a steamfitter and worked hard at his job. But they were both too young to accept the responsibilities of marriage.

The children came along fairly regularly, and when her family was old enough, Elizabeth got a job as a school crossing guard at the school. Near her post was a friendly neighborhood tavern, and Elizabeth got the habit of stopping in for just one after she was through with her work.

She soon began to feel at home in the tavern and

stayed longer and longer. She began to show up earlier for work, too—so she could have "just one" with her friends before starting. Although she only drank beer, she soon became addicted. Her children were neglected, and they became the butt of cruel jokes from the rest of the children at school. Of course, she was released from her job, but she still visited the tavern every day.

Her non-understanding husband soon left her and the children flat. He moved in with another woman in the same town, which only increased Elizabeth's shame and hatred. She drank more and more, and her children ate only because of the pastor and the local welfare worker. Her family totally disowned her; she was a complete outcast.

One day her priest finally persuaded her to go to the state hospital for help. He saw that her children were cared for and encouraged her to stay as long as she had to. There she had her first psychiatric counseling and her first contact with Alcoholics Anonymous. It took Elizabeth a long time to overcome her physical craving for alcohol, and an even longer time to get over her guilt and remorse. She had badly abused her children, though she still kept them with her physically.

She went to A.A. meetings on a fairly regular basis when she was released from the hospital. The doctor and priest explained her disease to her children. She made a very slow recovery from alcoholism, slipping back several times out of loneliness and fear. At this telling, she has been sober for two years.

She trained as a practical nurse and now works regularly in her profession. She never sees her husband, although they are not divorced. She and her children live on what she makes as a nurse and whatever the children can contribute from odd jobs. Hers was a fast fall and a slow recovery, but she was lucky in that her children tried to understand and were willing to help. She now feels that she has something to live for, and is trying to live now one day at a time.

In this stage your appearance has degenerated completely. Your person is never really clean. Your makeup, if any, is a smeary mess. Your eyes are glazed and unseeing. Your body is shaped like an old sack. Your clothes are dirty, ripped, and foul-smelling. Your teeth may be coated and missing. Your hair is lanky and greasy. Your feet won't carry you where you are trying to go. You may be covered with bruises, burns, cuts. You may have broken limbs. You may not even get out of bed. You may be drinking around the clock. The greatest effort you can make is to reach for the bottle thrown under the bed, or to grope for the pills on the night table. You have long since ceased to care about yourself, your husband, or your family. Emotionally, you alternate between arrogance and cringing fear. You are useless— to yourself, to your family, and to society. You have chosen the alcoholic road. Alcoholism is the only disease where the victim can be patient and doctor, can choose to be cured or not; the only disease, indeed, where the victim must choose for herself to be cured. No one else can do it for you.

Unless you choose to die—and the choice is now close at hand—you must give up. Your alcoholic arrogance must go; you must surrender. You must admit you are powerless over alcohol and pills and seek help. Remember: the choice is yours and yours alone. You must not and cannot lie to yourself. You cannot do it for anyone else, no matter how dear. It is the first step on the road back. Surrender and search. If, by any chance you still do not believe you are alcoholic, it may be impressed on you from the inside of a barred window in a mental institution. Or it may never be impressed on you at all. Your next stop may be a funeral home.

Where and how do you seek help? It is as close as your telephone. Look up Alcoholics Anonymous in your phone book. Call them; they will tell you what to do. Dial the operator if you can't focus on a phone book. If you do not have the moral courage to do this, call your doctor—and tell him the truth. If he has seen you lately you won't have to tell him much. Call the National Council on Alcoholism; they have branches all over the country. Call your local psychiatric hospital or your nearest psychiatric out-patient clinic. Call a friend you know is in A.A. Call your minister or priest or rabbi. But call. That single phone call is your open door to a new life, to new health, to new hope. It is a call you must make yourself. No one else's calling can help you.

# PART
# TWO

# The
# Way
# Out

# X

# Alcoholics

# Anonymous

THIS IS not a book about Alcoholics Anonymous. There are many books on that subject in your library: *Alcoholics Anonymous, Twelve Steps and Twelve Traditions,* and many others. This chapter will merely attempt to point out what A.A. has done for thousands of other women and girls, and what it can do for you.

A.A. is a fellowship of men and women who share their experience, strength, and hope with each other that they may solve their common problem and help others to recover from alcoholism.

The only requirement for membership is a desire to stop drinking. There are no dues or fees for A.A. membership; the organization is self-supporting through members' contributions. A.A. is not allied with any sect, denomination, political party, organization, or institution; it does not wish to engage in any controversy; nor does it endorse or oppose any cause. Its primary purpose is to have its members stay sober and to help other alcoholics achieve sobriety.

The only way you join A.A. is through your own efforts. Again, you cannot sober up for anyone else; you must do it for yourself. Other people can and will help you; but the desire to do so must be yours and yours alone. All you have to do to get help from A.A. is to call the nearest A.A. Intergroup office. It's listed in your telephone book under A.A. The man or woman on the other end of the wire will tell you what to do. It is so simple, yet so many people resist it. Why?

The nature of the woman alcoholic causes her to lie to herself. It is part of the disease—this inability to face reality, to recognize truth and to cope with it. Many women do not believe they are alcoholic; if they suspect they are, or are secretly afraid they are, they do not believe any one else knows. This is pure, unadulterated nonsense. You know when you are alcoholic; throwing up false barriers by denying symptoms—e.g., I don't drink until five o'clock; I don't drink in the morning; etc.—isn't going to change your alcoholism one bit.

Other people know, too. Your family was probably aware of your disease before you were; your strange behavior has not gone unnoticed in your office, your golf club, or your school. PEOPLE KNOW!

Yet many women resist joining A.A. because they feel everyone will then tag them as alcoholic. Since no one knows they drink, they figure why should anyone know they are hanging out with a bunch of drunks. Stop lying to yourself! People know you drink.

Note that if and when you join A.A., its members are just as anxious for anonymity as you are. They are not going to run around gossiping that Susie Jones or Mary Kelly has come to A.A. They are only there to help you, not to spread word of your disease around town. You may also be shocked to discover that many of your friends, long missing from the drinking scene, are waiting for you inside the doors of A.A. They will welcome you; they are truly glad to see you. There is nothing to be ashamed of in calling A.A. On the contrary, you are displaying moral courage and intelligence in doing something about your drinking. Many women simply do not have the guts to call A.A. Don't be one of them.

Another reason many women resist calling is they feel when they do, their lives are over. They are giving up fun and joy and parties and good times and a whole great, glorious, wonderful world. Any non-alcoholic reading this simply won't believe it, but it's true. This is the way alcoholics delude themselves. Let me tell you what you are giving up when you give up your drinking, if you are alcoholic:

> You are giving up your terrible, excoriating loneliness.
>
> You are giving up all the unnamed and hideous fears with which you have been living, all the deadening anxieties which prevent you from functioning as a normal human being.
>
> You are giving up the personality change which your alcoholism has caused in you.
>
> You are giving up days and nights alone in a miasma of fear and mistakes.
>
> You are giving up your acquired ugliness, both physical and emotional.
>
> You are giving up your fat and your fogginess.
>
> You are giving up screaming, fighting, hatred, self-doubt, self-pity, resentment, hostility, self-loathing.

You are giving up having people avoid you, having people do anything rather than invite you to their homes.

You are giving up having people closest to you say you are a moral leper with no backbone and no guts.

You are giving up not caring about how you look, how you feel, how you act.

You are giving up suicide as the only solution to your problems.

You are giving up having as the only single, primary concern in your life, a drink!

What are you getting in exchange? If you join A.A. the sober alcoholics there will give you, first of all, understanding and help. They will be your friends. And you have been without friends for a long time. They will slowly and patiently teach you the hows and whys of alcoholism, and what to do about it. When you feel you must have a drink, there will be another A.A. at the end of your telephone to help you overcome your compulsion. They will provide you with ways to get hospitalization if you need it. They are the one group on earth who know what makes you tick. And they are the one group you cannot fool.

You may be able to fool your doctor, your psychiatrist or psychologist, your mother, father, and husband, into thinking you are not going to drink anymore or that you are not drinking or taking pills now—even though you are. But you cannot fool an A.A. It is impossible to fool another alcoholic who has been there before you, who knows all the ins and outs, all the whys and wherefores, all the tricks and lies of your mutual disease. This is one of the major reasons why A.A. works when other methods do not.

But, before Alcoholics Anonymous can work for you, or for anyone, you must have a real desire to stop drinking for yourself. If you can have at least that much, plus a little honesty with yourself—which isn't so easy when you've lied to yourself all these years—A.A. will work for you.

A.A. will not work for people who merely use it as a tool to get off the hook. It will not work for people who do not have an honest desire to stop drinking, who wish to use A.A. as a crutch to get out of scrapes until they can have their next drink. Sometimes it will not work for women who have serious mental illnesses coupled with their alcoholism. But even then it will help them to stop drinking so something can be done about the other problems.

A.A. will not work for people who do not want it to work. This is the reason you may hear of women who have tried A.A. and failed. A.A. does not fail people; people fail A.A.

A.A. will not give you what you haven't got to begin with. It will not give you brains if you are stupid; it will not give you beauty if you are ugly; it will not give you health if you are ill; it will not give you money if you are poor; nor a husband nor a job.

What A.A. will give you is the ability to discover all the good things within yourself. It will give you a chance to use the brains you had to begin with and to use them wisely. It will restore you to sanity; it will give you a chance to restore yourself to health, physical and mental and spiritual. It will help you get a job commensurate with your abilities when you are sober enough to realize what you can do. It will help you make the most of the looks you have left, or prevent your destroying them further.

A.A. will help you through the traumas of everyday living, if you use it correctly. It will give you friends and fun. Yes, fun. The biggest shock you may have is to find out all the fun you can have without alcohol. Contrary to what you may expect about A.A., it is not a psalm-singing, breast-beating, drum-thwanging outfit. It is full of marvelous, good-looking, brainy, fun people with the supreme ability to laugh at themselves. You will not have enough time to go to all the parties, the dinners and dances, the engagements you will find at A.A.

You may wonder what you are going to do with all the time you spent drinking. You will fill it discovering yourself, the world around you, the people who are so great; in short, all the things you have been missing for so long.

In A.A. you will learn to stay away from a drink one day at a time. In the beginning it may be very difficult, especially if you are also taking pills. You will learn to give those up, too. You will find it easier each and every day. Sobriety, like alcoholism, is progressive. You will have help every step of the way. Medical help, if you need it. Psychiatric help, if you need that. Most of all it will be help from people who were probably a great deal worse off than you are when they joined A.A.

In A.A. you will learn to have peace of mind, peace of body, and peace of soul. You will learn to cope with problems without drinking or popping pills. You will grow in serenity. You will lose your self-pity and your resentments. You will meet people who are quite extraordinary, people who cope with problems you never faced. You will learn to allow yourself the luxury of a mistake. You will learn how to cope with and lose your guilt, remorse, and shame. You will learn how to forgive yourself, one of the most difficult things for an alcoholic to do. You will learn not to demand too much of yourself, how to channel your perfectionist demands. You will learn to choose between what is right and wrong for you; the choice will soon become automatic. In A.A. you will learn a whole new way of life, surrounded by the very people you may have wanted so desperately to meet through your drinking. A.A. is all things to all people. But only insofar as you give yourself to it.

As they say in A.A., you must learn to work the program. You can only learn this by going to meetings, constantly and regularly. You can only learn this by listening, by stopping shooting off your alcoholic mouth. If you feel you are not a joiner, that all this sweetness and light isn't for you, don't knock it until you've tried it. If you don't find what you want in one group, go to another. Water seeks its own level; you will find a group in which you will be happy if you truly look. God helps those who help themselves. You will only get out of A.A. what you put into it. Those people can only show you how; they cannot and will not do it for you.

The movement is no longer filled with Bowery Bums, tragic specimens of alcoholism. It is crowded today with young, brainy women learning how to live. They caught their disease before they destroyed everything; you can do the same. If you are still filled with the old superstitions and whispered rumblings about people who join A.A., go and look for yourself. You will be stunned. You will not be able to tell the alcoholics from the non-alcoholic visitors. If you are ashamed to go in your own community, go to a nearby one. They will understand.

If you live in a big city there is probably an A.A. meeting every night of the week. No one will talk *about* you; they will only talk *to* you.

You are giving up death and destruction. You are gaining life itself. Don't be a fool and throw it all away through superstitious shame and fear; make that phone call. It's the one call you will never regret!

# XI

# Other

# Ways Out

PSYCHIATRY works for some alcoholics, not for others. You should consult with your own doctor before approaching therapy with a psychiatrist. You may obtain pamphlets on psychiatry and its role in alcoholism from the National Council on Alcoholism, 2 East 103rd Street, New York, New York 10029.

Basically, the theories about the cause of alcoholism are many, probably as many as there are doctors, social workers, psychiatrists, and alcoholics themselves. Generally, they all agree that alcohol is used to satisfy a great need. Dependency then develops, cancels out other interests, and starts a vicious circle.

The alcoholic's need causes psychic pain, for which he uses more alcohol as an anesthesic. When the "cure" becomes worse than the pain, the alcoholic probably will look for help. This brings us to the question of motivation or what makes an alcoholic stop drinking.

Conversely the question is what causes him to resist sobriety, to maintain his drinking pattern?

Each person, alcoholic or non-alcoholic, has as part of his makeup certain defense mechanisms. These enable him to ward off psychic pain and bruises, the battering of everyday living. Alcoholics, often deeply guilty, condemned by mankind and themselves, drink compulsively and self-destructively.

Dr. Sidney Vogel, who is on the Advisory Board of ACCEPT and on the Executive Board of the New York City Medical Society on Alcoholism says that the defense mechanisms seen most frequently in the alcoholic character structure are: projection, denial, and rationalization. "Projection is a mental mechanism by means of which the individual's objectionable qualities, ideas, wishes and characteristics are not acknowledged as his own but are attributed to others or to his environment." (Sidney Vogel, MD—"Some Aspects of Group Psychotherapy with Alcoholics," and "An Interpretation of Medical and Psychiatric Approaches in the Treatment of Alcoholism") The alcoholic is scared, alone, immature, and basically suspicious. Instead of going to a doctor to relieve him of these symptoms, he uses the much quicker pain killer—alcohol. It is his defense against the world. It assuages his pain, but it also prolongs his hostility, his resentment, and his self-pity.

"Denial is a defense mechanism by means of which reality is erased or tailored to a new pattern. . . . In denial, the painful or unpleasant is actually not felt as such, nor is there an awareness of it. It has been transformed or displaced into something else." (Vogel) With an alcoholic, this is tied up with rationalization. Almost every alcoholic will deny the severity of his problem— how much he drinks, how often, how long. He will, of course, lie to himself first. He blames everyone and everything except himself. "Alcohol plays such a part in his life—like the complaints of the hypochondriac or the delusions of the paranoid personality—that any attempt to rid him of his alcoholism becomes a threat." (Vogel)

It is the rare alcoholic who goes to a psychiatrist completely voluntarily. He or she is usually pressured by family, friends, clergyman, employer, doctor, or life situation. The one who goes on his own probably has a better chance of doing something about his alcoholism more quickly than the others. The pressured ones often deny they really have a problem with alcohol; they are only there for help to "get through" a trying time in their lives. "Problems, including his hostilities, so common in all patients, but so intense and repressed in many alcoholics, can be bared. . . . The cathartic process, development of transference relationships, insight, ego strengthening, and finally reality testing, are, in essence, the basis of group psychotherapy." (Vogel) The good therapist knows the alcoholic feels less insecure in a group.

As with Alcoholics Anonymous, one of the most valuable contributions group therapy can make to an alcoholic is the realization that he or she is not alone with his problems. A therapy group can give an alcoholic enormous insight into his problems and, through mutual support, can help him to overcome them. It is important to note, too, that when an alcoholic seeks help, it should be given by the therapist as rapidly as possible. Otherwise the alcoholic, ego-bruised and battered as she is, will again feel rejected. Many doctors feel they can help a patient who is still drinking. I think it is nearly impossible, because of the indigenous alcoholic inability to discern and tell the truth in any form and to any degree.

The late Dr. Harry Tiebout, a pioneer in the treatment of alcoholics and an extremely able doctor in the field of alcoholism, felt that psychiatry had not carried its weight in the treatment of alcoholics. ". . . study and investigation of the condition had been hampered by inadequate opportunities for close and prolonged contacts." ("The Role of Psychiatry in the Field of Alcoholism, With Comment on the Concept of Alcoholism as Symptom and as Disease") Also, ". . . part of the failure to come to grips with alcoholism lay in faulty assumptions about the nature of the ailment." In other words, many psychiatrists feel alcoholism is merely a symptom of a more serious underlying disease and treat it as a symptom rather than a disease. In some cases this may very well be so. However, comparing alcoholism to cancer: regardless of cause, the cancer itself must be removed. The same is true of alcoholism. ". . . Alcoholics Anonymous whose program of ignoring the issue of causation and focusing directly on the drinking itself brings that behavior to a complete halt in an impressive percentage of alcoholics." (Tiebout) However, the number of psychiatrists who recognize alcoholism for the disease it is and are treating it as such is on the increase today.

As a layman, I would like to suggest also that many psychiatrists do not recognize the danger in substituting pills for alcohol. To calm an alcoholic patient, a psychiatrist may prescribe a tranquilizer or a sedative. The patient then often exchanges one hideous addiction for another. As the late Dr. E. M. Jellinek of Yale said: "The alcoholic who uses barbiturates is eating his alcohol instead of drinking it." This can only wind up in continued removal from reality, hopitalization, difficult withdrawal, or death. Lately more doctors are recognizing the pill addiction problem and are refusing to prescribe indiscriminately.

There are two main ways in which psychiatry, either solitary interviews or group therapy, can work. Basically, an alcoholic is a poor subject for analysis. Analysis is a long, hard piece of work, and the alcoholic personality is simply not stable enough to withstand the shocks and traumas—the truth. Many alcoholics are quite weak. They do not have the strength to go directly to Alcoholics Anonymous. Or they believe their alcoholism is not their own fault or, perhaps, that alcohol is not their main problem. A psychiatrist can help them overcome their inner fears and weaknesses, can offer supportive therapy long enough to enable the patient to stand on her own and gain the insight and courage necessary to do something herself about her drinking—which, of course, is the only road back there really is.

When the alcoholic is sober through her own efforts, a psychiatrist can be invaluable in helping her rid herself of her fears, neuroses, and anxieties, which contributed to her alcoholism in the first place. He can offer her medical help. He can give her vitamins that she may need, medication that may help restore her to health. He can introduce her to other alcoholics with simliar problems through group therapy. He can give her a sense of belonging and a place to go before she becomes desperate enough to drink again. He can prevent her falling into the hands of charlatans with wild and flighty theories and ridiculous "cures." He can advise her and help her to make herself whole again, and to take up her life as a functioning woman. He can give her an understanding of herself. But he cannot make her sober. Only she can do that for herself.

Before you decide upon psychiatric help, check the National Council on Alcoholism for their list of doctors interested in and able to help alcoholics. It will save you and the doctor a lot of time. It will also save you a lot of money. And, remember, no doctor can help you when you lie to him. Stop drinking; then see a doctor!

I believe unequivocally, that religion alone, applied as an exterior force, will not work for an alcoholic. There are many reasons. First of all, by the time an alcoholic woman seeks help—and that is usually much later than a man because she is a sneak about her drinking—her religion does not exist for her. You cannot turn religion on and off like a faucet. If she has ignored it and blasphemed against it for years, it will not come rushing to her aid merely because she calls.

The old saying that God helps those who help themselves is still quite true. No matter what the clergy in certain areas say, alcoholism has nothing whatsoever to do with will power. There are many alcoholics who would give their right arms to be able to stop drinking, if they could. Yet they cannot do it alone. Alcoholism is a disease—of the body, the mind, and the spirit. Religion, the spiritual control of life, can help in only one area. How many pledges have been made only to be broken!

However, religion may aid an alcoholic in seeking help. A priest or minister or rabbi may guide an alcoholic to A.A. or may suggest to a girl on pills that she see a psychiatrist. Many people in A.A. say they have had a spiritual awakening on joining A.A., although it is most certainly not a religious program. They feel some force or power higher than themselves guided them to it; and it is one of their beliefs that because they admit they are powerless over alcohol, this higher power will aid them to overcome their helplessness.

Today, religion is frequently not a very important part of a girl's life. It may be a subject she studies along with math and physics in school; it may assume a sort of vague, humanitarian aspect consisting of doing good and thinking positive thoughts. It is hardly a sweeping force strong enough to overwhelm the agonies and destruction of this disease in this day in the atomic age.

Using the opposition's own evidence, if religion alone were the answer to alcoholism, there would be no priests nor ministers with a drinking problem. Yet there are thousands upon thousands. Some of them in A.A. have told me they could not understand why their religion alone did not work for them; they felt perhaps they failed their churches; their churches did not fail them. Frustrations, anxieties, and failure are not the exclusive province of the non-religious; those whose lives are dedicated to God suffer them as well. But to a man, these priests and ministers felt they were better men of God for having suffered their alcoholism and done something about it. It gave them greater understanding and the ability to help others.

Upon achieving sobriety, many women discover a sense of peace they never had before, even as children. Some renew their religious tenets and become better church members than they had ever been. Many discover a communion with God they never had; they feel this higher power they discovered is with them all the time. Still others live out their lives as atheists. They are too independent ever to become involved with a reli-

gion, no matter how simple. That is their privilege and
private business.

In short, if you are counting on prayer and good
works alone to dig you out of the mess you have made
for yourself, if you think religion alone will enable you
to stop drinking or taking pills once you are addicted
you couldn't be more wrong. Religion will help you;
alone it cannot cure your disease.

The first thing many women of means do upon becoming alcoholic is to pop themselves into expensive
drying out places, sometimes euphemistically called
sanitariums. There are literally thousands of sanitariums across the face of this nation. Some are excellent;
some are deplorable. Some bask under the name of
beauty and health farms, although not all of these are
sanitaria. Some are little city convalescent hospitals,
where the same women keep going year after year after
year. Some are expensive psychiatric hospitals, where
alcoholic treatment is only incidental, where it is common to have one's friends or relations slip in a bottle
when the nurse is not looking. Some are old country
estates and manor houses turned into "alcoholic treatment centers" by people who don't know the first thing
about alcoholism and its treatment but who know it is an
extremely profitable way to make a living. Some are
farms endorsed by Alcoholics Anonymous which do not
tolerate or encourage repeaters, and which are excellent. Do you need a sanitarium? If so, how do you
choose one?

Generally speaking, I am opposed to the sanitarium
route of sobriety. In some cases, in cities where there
are no alcoholic hospitals or alcoholic wards in general
hospitals, they are vitally necessary. A sick alcoholic

must go some place to get well. Since many members of
the medical profession do not recognize alcoholism as a
disease, there are distressingly few hospitals that know
what to do for an alcoholic and how to do it. They can
treat the physical symptoms of alcoholism: the delirium
tremens; the malnutrition; the alcoholic neuritis; the
cuts, bruises, and lacerations; and dreadful hangovers;
the vitamin deficiencies. But then what? Of necessity,
they must turn the patient out into the street—to drink
again, to pop her pills again. Supportive therapy is
almost non-existent.

That is why many alcoholic drying out places sprang
up in the first place. Naturally, if you are rich you will
be well-treated. They will withdraw you from your little
bottle gradually; it's called tapering off. You will be
filled with drugs and sedatives to ease the pain of your
hangovers. You will be coddled and cosseted and sent
forth thinner, shinier, and ready to drink again. You
will soon be back.

Some women have standing reservations in such
gilded sanitariums. They use them as crutches when
their daily lives get to be too much for them. The sanitariums get them off the hook. As long as they keep using this crutch, it is in the insidious nature of their
disease that they will not get sober. There is no motivation, no reason. The only times women like these really
make an effort to get sober is when they get sick and
tired of being sick and tired.

Repeaters are the life's blood of the sanitarium game.
It was very interesting to me to discover that at one of
the most expensive "farms" in the country, chockfull of
rich drunks, the only time several of the patients went
out and did something about their diseases was when
their money ran out.

Should you decide that you need a few weeks at a sanitarium before you can pick up the threads of your life again, this time without alcohol, take heart. There are several very good ones run by dedicated men and women whose only interest in life is the welfare of the alcoholic patient. These are the unsung heroes in a class with missionaries and martyrs. You can very easily tell the difference between these good ones and the others. They will not encourage you to return; and their fees are reasonable. Their accoutrements are not plush; they are not geared to coddle you and make you beautiful. They are there to help you stand on your own two feet without alcohol and pills. You can find them by ringing the Alcoholics Anonymous Intergroup Office in your city, or by consulting your own doctor, who will check on one such place for you.

If you choose this route to sobriety, do not use it as a crutch. Do not go with the intention of returning when you have to, when you need it. You will never get sober that way. You will return again and again, until your money runs out, or until your family and your doctor lose patience and hope for you. Then it's the state hospital, which might have done you more good in the first place. Sanitariums can be a help in certain cases. They are a means to an end: sobriety. They are not an end in themselves.

To sober up on one's own, without help, is the most difficult path of all to sobriety. It can be done; it has been done; it will be done. But I have never understood why. Sobering up on one's own is the cause célèbre of the famous "reformed" drunk: dour, dedicated, intolerant, and inflexible. These are the women who are "dry" as opposed to sober. They do not drink; they are proud of it. Their whole lives revolve around this fact; there is little else that interests them. Their sense of humor is nonexistent. They look down their noses at other alcoholic women who get help. They feel they have backbone, guts, and will power that other women don't have. Maybe they do. But they also have with them still the things that caused their alcoholism in the first place: their loneliness, perhaps their aggressiveness, their insecurity and lack of confidence, their dislike of other people, their inability to make friends, and their general lack of interest in anything that doesn't smack of alcoholism and its cure. These are the crusaders for prohibition; these are the women who don't go to cocktail parties, who don't give them, who consider themselves a cut above everyone else. They have stopped drinking physically; that is all they have done. They have not learned how to live, nor how to love. Their chances of drinking again are very good indeed. They miss alcohol; they have not really lost the compulsion to drink. A good push will send them over the edge. And they will be worse off than they ever were before. Any alcoholic can stop drinking for a time. It is no sign of the arrest of the disease that you are not drinking right now. A non-alcoholic doesn't have to stop drinking from time to time; she doesn't even think about it.

If you choose to get sober on your own, go right ahead. It's your choice. But don't be surprised to find yourself reaching for that glass of whiskey before bedtime instead of your much-vaunted glass of milk. No woman is an island; your pride, ego and neurotic tendencies are still with you. Drinking is here to stay, whether you can be part of it or not. This way you will be fighting it all alone and sobriety is *no* place to be all alone.

# XII

# What's

# Being Done

At Rutgers, the State University of New Jersey, there exists the Center of Alcohol Studies. This school is a pioneer and a leader in the study of alcoholism. The editorial offices of the *Quarterly Journal of Studies on Alcohol* are at Rutgers. This *Journal* is a repository for the reports of new research on all aspects of alcohol and alcoholic problems. It is published for all who are interested in these subjects, not for any special group. Original articles report the findings of research workers in the fields of medicine, physiology, biochemistry, psychiatry, psychology, pathology, sociology, economics, statistics, education, law, and other disciplines and professions. It publishes current literature on the subject as well as an annual index. The *Journal* is an integral part of the total documentation system for the field of alcohol studies maintained by the Rutgers Center.

The Publications Division of the Rutgers Center also

prints and reprints popular, technical, and nontechnical books and pamphlets on all aspects of alcohol problems. These include literature on psychology and psychiatry, treatment, public health, the family, industry, social problems, and cultural patterns.

Each year the university conducts The Summer School of Alcohol Studies. Since the School was founded at Yale University in 1943, over 4,500 students have attended. They have come from the fifty states, the ten Canadian provinces, and twenty-seven other countries. Because of the broad geographic distribution, the wide range of professional backgrounds, experience, and interests the informal interaction among each year's student body has provided wide and valuable experience in itself.

Two programs are offered: The Physicians' Institute, which covers the principles and practices of comprehensive treatment of alcoholics, and the Course Program. This latter includes:

The function and structure of alcoholism services for doctors, nurses, psychologists, social workers.

The implications of alcohol use for school and community for primary, secondary and college teachers and for educational directors.

Social casework with alcoholics and their families for social workers.

An introduction to counseling for those who have some responsibility in counseling alcoholics.

Counseling in alcoholism for those who have had some counseling experience but no formal, structured foundation.

Organizing and developing alcoholism programs

in a public-health setting for public-health administrators.

Organizing and administering community programs.

Nursing services to alcoholic patients for nurses.

Alcoholism and public-health nursing for public-health nurses.

Institutional programs for the homeless alcoholic for halfway house administrators, institutional chaplains, mission directors, and Salvation Army officers.

Problems in correctional responses to drinking behavior for police and court officers.

Pastoral counseling with alcoholics and their families for clergymen.

Labor-management approaches to alcoholism for labor and management personnel.

Also at Rutgers, The Northeast Institute of Alcoholic Studies, co-sponsored by the official State Alcoholism Programs of nine northeastern states, is held. This Institute provides a general overview of problems of alcohol and alcoholism for board members of official and voluntary agencies, civic leaders, and others without special training or experience in this field, and for persons with professional qualifications who have little acquaintance with the field or who are unable to devote more than a week to such study.

Although Rutgers is the most famous, other universities across the nation have or are instituting courses of study in this field.

The medical profession is about fifty years behind the times in the treatment of alcoholism. In medical treatment, alcoholism as a disease stands today where tuberculosis stood in America around 1900. It wasn't until 1956 that the American Medical Association designated alcoholism as a medical problem and recognized it for the disease it is.

There are, however, a handful of doctors across the country who are dedicated men. One of them, perhaps one of the most famous in the East, told me that when he arranged lectures and a seminar at his medical school for interns to learn about alcoholism, only two men showed up. It is not a profitable nor a "dramatic" disease for doctors. They would much prefer to find a cure of cancer or heart trouble or schizophrenia. Yet, according to the United States Department of Health, Education and Welfare, "Approximately 5,000,000 Americans may be classified as alcoholics. Thus it may be stated that alcoholism is one of the more important domestic issues before us and that broad interprofessional–public action at every level of society will be required for its solution."

The State of New Jersey, perhaps because Rutgers is located there, has the State Department of Health send out a Treatment Digest for Physicians that is excellent. New Jersey also has many hospitals that *will* treat and *know how* to treat alcoholics.

New York State and New York City, so advanced in many areas, are a disgrace in treatment of alcoholics. If a police officer picks up a drunk on the streets of New York there is no place he can take him! John Murtagh, Criminal Court administrative judge and a member of the National Council on Alcoholism, has been fighting for years for help for these sick people. Recently, Judge Murtagh has had some success in having alcoholism looked on by the law as an illness instead of a criminal act. "He has called for revisions in the philosophy of criminal law "to confine it to conduct that disturbs others." In a speech before the National Council on Alcoholism the Judge said that arrests of drunks in New York "are truly becoming a thing of the past."

Most of the wards in private and city hospitals in New York that will take alcoholics have been pressured to do so by Alcoholics Anonymous and by the National Council on Alcoholism. At Bellevue Hospital, there is a new experimental unit working with disturbed patients, some of whom are alcoholic. The state hospitals will take alcoholics, if the patient signs herself in. I feel an alcoholic has to be pretty forlorn and hopeless before she will do this.

Many of the hospitals that will accept alcoholics for treatment are equipped only to treat male alcoholics. Recently there has been a breakthrough. The first voluntary treatment unit for women in the New York State Hospital system has been established at Central Islip, Long Island. It is patterned after a male unit that has been in operation for many years. "The center serves various kinds of women—housewives, divorcees, drifters who cannot hold a job, and even an occasional affluent woman whose analyst has failed her." It has a capacity of eighty patients; women pay according to their ability to do so.

Some dedicated doctors are working constantly in new areas of treatment for alcoholics. In a report before the Federation of American Societies for Experimental Biology, two doctors from the New Jersey Neuropsychiatric Institute reported "that the effects of alcoholic beverages were not limited to the main active ingredient —ethyl alcohol. Whiskies and other alcoholic beverages also contain traces of many other substances named congeners. These may play a significant role in the hangovers and chronic intoxication of alcoholics."

Certain endocrinologists are currently working on the disease known as hypo-glycemia (low blood sugar) and its connection with alcohol. These doctors feel it may cause a predisposition to alcoholism, and may have some relation to postalcoholic depression and general malaise. Others are working in the area of niacin treatments for alcoholism. A Minnesota cardiologist, Dr. Carl Alexander, has found the first distinguishing signs of alcoholic cardiopathy. Using the electron microscope, he has discovered cardiac changes thought to be unique to alcoholics. "The picture on the electron microscope resembles that seen in individuals who have been on generally deficient diets for a long time. The prognosis is good when alcoholic cardiopathy is detected early, but 'the disease often goes unrecognized or is misdiagnosed until late in its course, when it is irreversible and fatal within a short period of time.' "

But for every enlightened and dedicated doctor, there are still too many who have little knowledge of alcoholism, too many who secretly still look upon this disease as a moral stigma not in their province. This is unfortunate, because the woman alcoholic especially often turns first to her doctor for help. The National Council on Alcoholism has local affiliates across the country. Its primary purpose is education and public information. It provides literature and advisory services. Its slogan is "to arouse public opinion and mobilize it for action." For further knowledge of this helpful organization, I refer you to Marty Mann's *New Primer on Alcoholism*.

In New York City there is a relatively new organization sponsored by the New York Council on Alcoholism. It is called ACCEPT—Alcoholism Center Coordinating

Education, Prevention and Treatment. Located at 167 East 80th Street, ACCEPT offers information, counseling, literature, psychiatric evaluation, individual and group therapy, and educational discussion groups. It provides referals to physicians, rest homes, hospitals, clergy, Alcoholics Anonymous, Al-Anon Family Groups, social agencies and other appropriate community resources. ACCEPT's services are available, without charge, to the problem drinker, the family, the employer, or the friend. Immediate counseling is provided and a recovery program is planned to meet the particular needs needs of the individual case. A clinical service combines the professional skills of a member of specialists.

I mention ACCEPT because I have seen their work. It is an organization of dedicated men and women, most of whom are volunteers. It should be an example of enlightened community thinking for other cities and towns.

In recent years the Federal government has become increasingly concerned with the problem of alcoholism. The seven agencies of the Department of Health, Education and Welfare are involved in combating this complex problem, and in doing research.

For example, the Vocational Rehabilitation Administration supports research and demonstration projects to help rehabilitate alcoholics. The Welfare Administration is providing services to help prevent alcoholism or to minimize its damaging effects on the family; and the Food and Drug Administration continues to wage a fight against the quackery of advertised cures for alcoholism.

The major portion of the government's research efforts in this area, however, is centered at the National Institute of Mental Health of the Public Health Service.

Current research includes the study of such basic

problems as the metabolism of alcohol, and the effects of alcohol on the central nervous system and on personality.

One project supported by the NIMH is the Cooperative Commission on the Study of Alcoholism at the Institute for the Study of Human Problems at Stanford University. The Commission's major tasks are:

> To assess the current status of research knowledge.
> To evaluate alcoholism programs and resources.
> To study the relationships between alcoholism organizations.
> To make recommendations for improving treatment, education, and prevention.

The NIMH also supports several important training programs that pertain specifically to alcoholism. One acquaints casework students with treatment and rehabilitation programs. Another is a pilot project preparing pre-doctoral social science students through research and seminar activities for work in alcoholism.

In 1964 the Health, Education and Welfare Department Committee on Alcoholism was appointed to recommend and co-ordinate department activities and objectives in the field of alcoholism. In the same year the National Institute of Mental Health established a Section on Alcoholism and Drug Abuse to foster increased attention on program planning; to provide more technical assistance and consultation to public and private agencies; and to encourage improved research, evaluation, treatment, rehabilitation, and other aspects of a comprehensive approach to the alcoholism problem.

Concern with new and untried drugs in the treatment of alcoholism is not in the province of this book. It is always dangerous to list drugs where alcoholics are concerned, because it is in the nature of the alcoholic to clutch at anything that will enable her to continue her drinking while alleviating her pain. It is also true that drugs are the concern of the medical profession, and their choice and administration should be left to doctors.

For physicians who are interested, and it is to be hoped that many of them are, information and study may be obtained through the *Quarterly Journal of Studies on Alcohol* of Rutgers University. This *Journal* reports that the number of psychotherapeutic agents available for the management of alcoholism continues to increase. However, double blind tests, in which neither the doctor nor the patient knows if a given patient is receiving a drug or a harmless placebo, have proven that there was no apparent advantage in giving the active drugs as compared to the placebo. This may again indicate that the knowledgeable and sympathetic ear of a good doctor is more valuable than the most "perfect" drug.

The New Jersey State Department of Health Treatment Digest for Physicians, which is condensed from the *Quarterly Journal of Studies on Alcohol* says: "The variety of psychotherapeutic agents available for the management of alcoholism continues to increase. However, double blind tests have proven that no advantage of the active drugs was apparent as compared to the placebo."

The *Journal* reports clinical studies with non-habituating drugs useful for the alleviation of acute withdrawal symptoms, as well as in the control of anxiety during sobriety. It indicates drugs for use with patients who are agitated, compulsive, and who tend to manifest their complaints through physical ills. Some drugs, which

113

have been in common use, have been reported to be potentially habituating. Some have brought on agitated depression and the return of a craving for alcohol.

Dr. Vernelle Fox reports in clinical studies with private alcoholic patients at the Peachtree Hospital and with alcoholic patients at the Georgian Clinic in Atlanta: "The phenothiazines, particularly promazine, chlorpromazine, triflupromazine and fluphenazine are the most useful. Nonhabituating, these drugs are particularly useful for the alleviation of acute withdrawal symptoms as well as in the control of anxiety during sobriety. They potentiate the sedative effect of the alcohol in the patient's system without producing agitated depression as barbiturates do. . . ."

For office treatment of the alcoholic, especially those alcoholics who really haven't decided to stop drinking, Fox and her associates found the diphenylmethane derivative, hydroxyzine, to be the most effective. It is safe in that it alleviates the dangers involved when the patient starts drinking again after leaving the office. It is also a good drug for the patient who is severely debilitated or who has cardiovascular disease. Other drugs these doctors have tested have proven hallucinogenic.

For the acutely ill: Interestingly, a higher proportion of women than men responded well to treatment with the dibenzazepine derivative, cyproheptadine. It has been particularly effective in the treatment of the agitated, compulsive patient who tends to manifest his complaints in physical ills.

For the control of acute withdrawal symptoms, Fox and her associates found drugs such as meprobamate oxanamide, diazepam, and others alone, or in combination with the phenothiazines, effective as sedatives. Because of their intoxicating and potentially habituating properties, however, these drugs are not used for the control of anxiety. They have also observed that methaminodiaxzepoxide brought out agitated depression in some patients.

Disulfiram has been reported as being valuable in the maintenance program of many patients; about fifteen percent used it voluntarily sometime during their recovery. Disulfiram, known to many Americans as Antabuse, works best with patients who are strongly motivated toward becoming sober. Dr. Ruth Fox, in her pamphlet, "Treatment of Chronic Alcoholism," says, "Disulfiram acts as an external control for which the patient is often grateful. . . . Only one decision a day need be made not to drink, i.e., on the taking of the pill, in contrast to the several hundred decisions . . . which the alcoholic trying to abstain on his own may be called on to make." Antabuse is not usually given to patients with marked emotional instability because they just won't stop drinking.

Flagyl is a new experimental drug which appears in some instances to remove the desire to drink. A social worker friend of mine told me this was the first drug which seemed to give alcoholics a profound sense of joy, which alcoholics rarely, if ever, have. Not enough is known about Flagyl yet to report any conclusive results.

The Pavlovian theory is the conditioned reflex or aversion theory. It has been in favor with some psychologists about twenty-five years. An injection of emetine is given. This produces nausea and vomiting, during which the alcoholic is forced to take a drink. A disgust for the taste and smell of liquor is supposed to develop by association. Anything at all that works for you should be tried. But I feel anything imposed from the outside doesn't stand a chance with the alcoholic. A.A. teaches you to get sober by staying away from alcohol one drink at a time and by living one day at a time. This comes from within, which is why it works. But drugs and Pavlov may prop you up while you are groping. If you decide you are emotionally geared for this reflex-action type of cure, be sure and consult a good reputable psychologist and not some quack.

Quacks and cults abound in the treatment of alcoholism. I have mentioned the expensive drying out places that are geared for return customers. There are lay preachers and yogi teachers, sun-worshippers, astrologers, and pseudo-religio-psychology pushers. In short there are as many phonies in the "quick cure for alcoholism" business as a helpless, emotionally unstable, confused, sick alcoholic can pay for. When you look for help, do not fall into their hands. Go to your own doctor, call the National Council on Alcoholism office near you, or call A.A. They are honest; they will help you. Do not believe that because one of these did not work for someone you know, they will not work for you. If you really want to stop drinking, any of these will work for you! If you do not, nothing will—neither psychiatry, nor drugs, nor mother love, nor jail, nor Alcoholics Anonymous will work! It's up to you!

# XIII

# Coming

# Out of It

SOBRIETY, like alcoholism, is progressive. Any well-motivated alcoholic probably will do well in any form of therapy. But what motivates an alcoholic?

No one will consider giving up alcohol until the pain, anguish, and suffering it causes is greater than the escape it provides. The further down you are on your slide, the tougher it is going to be to come back up again. And you must believe that eventually a life of sobriety, a life of honor, industry, and pleasure can be better and will be better than constantly recurring alcoholic crises.

If you go to Alcoholics Anonymous, or you are in group therapy, which is essentially the same thing, you will learn to use the tools that will keep you sober. You will learn to substitute giving, love, friendship, and hope for the negative qualities of cynicism, resentment, hatred, hostility, and frustration that made you an

117

alcoholic in the first place. But you must realize one thing: You can never drink again! This is a terrible shock, an unbelievable barrier, an emptiness which you have to face. You cannot drink, not sherry, creme de menthe, mouthwash, lemon extract—nothing! And you cannot substitute barbiturates for your drinks either. Because, by definition, an alcoholic is someone who cannot stop drinking or taking pills *once she has started.* You can abstain for any length of time, telling yourself secretly that you will be able to drink at some time in the future. Well, you can't. This rationalization, this lying to yourself is what causes the return to alcoholism. This is the reason you hear of people who cannot sober up in A.A. or with their psychiatrists. You must accept the fact that you are an alcoholic, and you must surrender to it. If you have any reservations, any doubts, if you are lying to yourself, you will drink and get drunk again—and again and again and again.

And, sobriety in and of itself—though it has many rewards—is not enough! This is why it is so difficult, so empty, so unrewarding and, really, so unnecessary to get and stay sober on your own, without help. Sobriety or, to call it by its right name, dryness, is only the beginning. With help, gradually, like a baby learning to crawl, you will learn to live again—really live, perhaps for the first time!

Dr. Harry Tiebout, as mentioned before, is a man famous for his treatment of alcoholics; in his "The Role of Psychiatry in the Field of Alcoholism," Dr. Tiebout says therapy must aim at helping the individual to learn to live with his limitation, namely, that she cannot drink normally. The alcoholic must be brought to accept that she is the victim of a disease, that the only way for her to remain healthy is to refrain from taking the first drink, the first pill. If she attempts to drink moderately, she may succeed for a time, but sooner or later the disease will be rekindled and she will be in trouble again.

Perhaps the first joy you will experience upon achieving sobriety is the ability to eat—to really taste and enjoy your food. It may have been years since you knew what you were eating. It will come as an unbelievable blessing, too, to awaken in the morning and know deep down inside that you realize where you were the night before, and what you did, and with whom. Gradually, very gradually, your fears will begin to fade—if you really work at your therapeutic program.

In A.A. they teach you to stay away from alcohol one day at a time. If you work the rest of the program, if you use it honestly and faithfully, you will soon lose your compulsion to drink. One day you will be shocked to discover that you haven't thought about alcohol or drinking at all for quite a while. This doesn't happen immediately, of course, but it does happen. Your anxieties will lessen; you will begin to adjust to the world around you; you will begin to be aware of what a fantastic world it really is and can be; in short, you will begin to assume your rightful place in the world; you have begun to grow up!

You may need individual psychiatric help after joining A.A. or going to group therapy sessions. By all means, get it—when you have stopped drinking. Therapy, plus what you will learn in A.A., will give you a greater understanding of yourself than you thought possible. You will soon realize that other people have problems, too—often far greater than yours. And they don't all run to a bottle or a pill to escape from them.

You will soon learn another fact of alcoholic life: When you join A.A., you must keep at it. It is not a life sentence, a juridical *must*; it is simply something that you should and will do. You will find yourself enjoying it enormously. A diabetic does not discontinue her insulin shots after treatment balances her system; she accepts as a fact of life that she must continue her treatment. So will you; only yours will be a lot more fun!

One of the greatest joys in the cessation of drinking is that now you can begin to work on your appearance. It's probably the greatest project you will ever undertake; it is continuous; and it is rewarding. Women who sober up by themselves usually miss this; they are too involved in keeping away from the bottle to think of anything else.

The first thing you will notice when you have stopped drinking for a while is your weight loss. The bloat will begin to go—even though you are eating more than you ever did. Your abdomen and stomach will shrink; your jowls will no longer flap. Naturally, you have shot your health by now. But alcoholics have unbelievable constitutions—and you will get your health back. Go to your doctor for a checkup; no one will be happier than he to see you, if he understands your problem. Chances are you will need vitamin shots, perhaps other medication to set your system to rights. Do what the doctor says; it's very important. And it will take time.

Another thing you must remember is not to get too tired or too hungry. If you do, you will think of a drink. Try and get yourself on a regular schedule for a while. Don't plunge into hysterical activity right away. Take it easy; first things first.

If you can't sleep well immediately, don't resort to pills. Walk a lot, go to A.A. meetings, exercise, and do your housework or your job. You will begin to be so tired normally that you can't stay awake. Insomnia never killed anyone; if you stay awake too long your body will eventually cry out for sleep. Let me repeat: Do *not* take pills to sleep! You are in no emotional or physical condition to substitute one addiction for another.

As you are slowly working your way out of your alcoholic debris, your early guilts will eventually begin to take on human proportions. You should learn to stop hating yourself, to begin to be good to yourself. For a woman, if you can afford it, one of the nicest things to do is to take yourself to a good beauty salon. You do not have to tell them you've been sick—they can probably see it for themselves anyhow. Get yourself a great haircut and set. If you've gone gray and hate it, get a good colorist to change it for you. Have a facial—you owe yourself at least one; it's such a superb, luxurious feeling. Have a massage, too; you'll feel great.

Learn how to use makeup, but don't overdo it. Read the fashion magazines; find out what's been going on in the world while you've been away. Your skin is probably a complete mess; ask the saleswoman at the cosmetic counter how to care for it or read magazine articles for advice. Invest in a good cream; use it. Use a foundation and eye makeup; try all the new products— blushers and highlighters. No one can use makeup camouflage more than you can. While your skin is still that sickly jaundiced yellow, use a rosy foundation. If your complexion has been bright red for years from liquor, you'll be surprised to see how fast the high color disappears.

If you are thin and undernourished, eat, eat, eat. Take vitamins; you need them. Keep yourself meticulously groomed at all times. You cannot afford to neglect yourself now in any way.

Go out and buy yourself some new clothes—even if you can't afford them. Reward yourself for being sober —why not? Throw away those hideous, dirty, ripped clothes that remind you of your drinking. Get yourself at least one pair of good shoes, one pair of decent white gloves, and a new bag. All this need not be expensive if you know how to shop, and you owe it to yourself to look your best.

Don't wallow around in the filth that reminds you of your drinking. Clean up your apartment or your house. It doesn't have to be glamorous, but it certainly can be clean.

And remember, Rome wasn't built in a day. You don't have to do it all at once. Hold out a shopping trip as a present to yourself for staying sober another day. If you have a lot of bills, and you probably do, don't worry. You will pay them. Go and see your creditors, if you feel you should, explain your problem and work out payments. They will be very grateful and may help you—you might be surprised. Then, go and get your new clothes; do *not* wear sackcloth and ashes as a penance. It will only prolong your self-hate, and that's not the way to get well.

As you get and remain sober, the change in your looks will astound you! Not only will you start to look immensely better physically, but the inner peace you begin to radiate will show. You will have new friends and a new life, and that alone will make you look better. The haunted, furtive look will disappear from your eyes. Your glazed expression will be gone—along with your fat and bad coloring. Get out in the sun, walk around, learn to live—one day at a time. What a great life you are going to have!

If you have been a working girl, single or married, chances are you are out of a job. Or, if you still have one, it's not a very good one. You may have gone back to live with your parents or other relatives, or you may be holed up alone in a flat where you can't pay the rent. Do not panic!

As you get sober, as your thinking clears up, you *will* get a job. If you are flat broke, borrow the money from someone to live until you are on your own two feet. You always managed to get money to drink; you can manage to get money to stay sober—even if it is from the government in the form of welfare or unemployment insurance. Your family will probably be glad to stake you once they see you are serious about your sobriety. Make the resolution, and keep it, that you will pay them back.

You have in front of you now the possibility of unlimited success. If you are an older working woman, who has blown her job, you *can* get another. Do not believe for one minute that it is hopeless. There are receptionists' jobs; there is a crying need for good secretaries—many men would put their arms in the fire for a good, responsible older gal secretary. These men are a bit tired of the "babies" who turn up only when they feel like it. If you have a profession, you can return to it. And, above all, you can retrain yourself for something, perhaps something you always wanted to do.

Julia was a mousy and timid girl from the Midwest. She had a number of brothers and sisters, most of whom she helped to support. She had gone to the state university and had become a librarian. Although she loved books, she hated the loneliness and inactivity of her life. She began to buy a bottle and take it home with her on Friday nights. Soon, she moved away from her family and took her own apartment. She began to take liquor home with her every night.

Years passed. Julia never married, primarily because she never met any eligible men in her job. If she did chance upon one, she was too enamored of her bottle, awaiting her at home, to spend much time listening to him. No one at her job really knew she drank. They felt something was radically wrong; but it isn't usual to suspect a small-town librarian of being alcoholic. Julia's looks were raddled; her thinking was pretty confused. But still she drank, never suspecting that liquor was the major problem she had.

She grew older and lonelier. One day she passed out at work. They took her to the local hospital, where a very shocked doctor discovered she had hardly any liver left and was actually in a chronic state of alcoholism. The doctor was kind enough and wise enough to keep his discovery to himself, but to tell Julia the facts; he recommended she seek therapy immediately. Julia resigned from her job and with her accumulated pension and savings went to the nearest large city, where no one knew her. There she did three things: She joined the local branch of Alcoholics Anonymous; she went into therapy with a good psychiatrist; and she enrolled in the graduate school of the city college. Julia had always loved children. She had never had any of her own; but she felt she could teach children well. And that is exactly what she did.

At the age of forty-seven she became a teacher in the

city public school system. She is still sober, still going to A.A. and her doctor, and is now reasonably happy in her teaching profession. Re-training was her answer to a new life.

If you are still young, you are perhaps a bit luckier than others. Your future lies ahead of you, and it is yours to make successful. Remember, you are probably quite bright; you can do anything you want to do. If you need money immediately, take the first decent job that comes along. You don't have to, nor will you, stay in it. But the ordinary routine of going to work every day like all those "normal" people is marvelous for you.

In a sense, women alcoholics are luckier in this way than men. They may have been drinking quietly and secretly and people don't know about their drinking history. If this is your case, don't feel obliged to tell them, many will not understand. A man who probably drank all over the lot and established a reputation for drinking will find it difficult to overcome. Also, you may not have been as high on the career scale as a man when you blew it. So you don't have to feed your ego by refusing to take a job not fit for your talents.

When you are first starting out, learn to keep your big mouth shut. Listen; don't talk. Don't project your ego all over the office just because you're sober. Lots of people are sober all of the time. Learn to do the menial, routine work; you must know how to do this before you can accept the responsibilities of a more challenging position. Do not expect to start off at the top—the world has gone by you while you were drinking—don't think you're going to plunge in and take over right away. But as you learn to cope, as you learn how excit-ing the world of business really can be, you will begin to extend your horizons. And you will also realize one day with a great start that your drinking and resultant sobriety, your efforts at a new way of life have given you a greater understanding of people and their problems. You will be more tolerant than you could have believed possible; you will know instinctively what makes people tick. It will help enormously in your future. You will also learn to roll with the punches, one thing few businesswomen really learn. You have been to hell and back; what can be so tough or awful about a business setback? This gives you a leg up on other women right away.

If you have been working for a while and feel you have gone as far as you can in your job, quit. Don't be afraid; you will get another, better one. You will know when to move on; it is when the routine of your present job is beginning to irritate you. You are getting well; you are ready for bigger and better things. You have a great capacity for work. Beware of one thing, however. Sober alcoholics have a tendency to do too much. They are driven; they want to make up for the years they lost. They will take on any job knowing they can do it. Learn your limitations as well as your capabilities. Stop demanding perfection of yourself; if you fail, you will get drunk.

If you are in communications or some allied field the pressures will be just as enormous as they were when they originally drove you to drink. This is, of course, true in other fields as well, but the tensions are more obvious in communications. You will have to learn to withstand these tensions. You will have to say to yourself over and over and over again: Easy does it; first things first. If you say it often enough it will soon work for you and you will adjust. You will learn what you must do, and what can be put off till tomorrow. Do not try to do it all; you cannot. No one can. If you don't drink, you may develop ulcers or have a heart attack. I have never known a really lazy alcoholic; the disease drives her to the other extreme. Live and let live. Learn to be tolerant; most of all of yourself.

Try and be objective rather than emotional about your job. Don't be so grateful to a boss who didn't fire you while you were drinking that you won't move on. Don't be afraid to sever ties with friendly co-workers. That is all a reversion to immaturity, and you must grow up. Know yourself; know what you can do. Then go and find a job that will enable you to do it. If the job you're in has possibilities, fine. Stay there and gradually assume more responsibility. If it's a dead end, get out. Boredom is just as treacherous as pressure to an ex-drunk.

If you are a nurse and you've always wanted to be a writer, write in your spare time. You may sell something, and you're on your way. Don't be afraid to take a chance; you pass this way only once. Grab at the banquet feast of life; remember, most people are starving to death.

One thing that will be restored to you with sobriety, if you are working your therapeutic program right, is your sense of humor. Outside of the world's richest and most indulgent father, this is probably the greatest asset a woman can have. It allows her to look at herself objectively, and at her place in the scheme of things. It is the one thing that certainly disappeared with her drinking. You can now allow yourself the "luxury" of a mistake, without self-condemnation. You can laugh at yourself and at the mistakes you have made and are making. You will not take yourself too seriously—

127

which is one of the most marvelous gifts you can have. It will make your life easier in every way; it will help you understand other people with whom, after all, you must live. It will help you in your job, especially if and when you lose it. It will help you understand the overall plan of life and your place in it. As an alcoholic, I urge you to learn to laugh at yourself. Usually, the more developed your sense of humor, the higher your intelligence anyway. It will give you profound joy to be able to laugh!

You may face the problem of overcoming a drinking reputation in business. This is not easy to do—and only one thing will do it. Continued sobriety. If you continue to show up at work and do a good job, sober, people will find out. They may be cynical in the beginning, and justly so. You have been sober for periods before perhaps, then gone on another drinking spree. This is a further reason why it is so difficult to stay sober on your own. If you are in therapy, and feel like drinking, someone will help you. If you can go to your boss and explain that you have joined A.A. or are working with a therapist, he or she (probably she) will certainly understand and help you.

Incidentally, if you have not gotten a reputation for drinking, I do not advise running around telling prospective employers that you are a sober alcoholic. Many of them will not understand and you will not get the job or the promotion. If you are lucky, and your present or future employer understands about alcoholism and A.A., he or she may take a chance on you. I have heard many employers say that no one is more reliable or dedicated than a sober alcoholic in A.A. But you may not be that lucky and may be creating unnecessary problems for yourself.

When people realize that you have been sober for quite a while, and that this time you mean it, they will be delighted. In the beginning, at office cocktail parties and luncheons, they may make a point of not asking you, or of rushing up to you with coffee or a soft drink. Laugh goodnaturedly and ignore it; this, too, shall pass. Besides, you will be very surprised indeed to discover how many people do not drink at these functions. They are usually the ones at the top. If anyone questions your not drinking, tell them you are allergic to alcohol or that you have a weight problem. The only ones who will make a fuss are the ones who have drinking problems themselves. Watch and see!

You didn't become alcoholic in a day; you will not establish or re-establish your sober position in business in a day either. But time and therapy are on your side; if you continue to stay sober and do a good job, you can't help but succeed. Problems that would have appeared insurmountable while drinking will be passed over with a laugh. If you are not careful you may wind up as president of the firm yourself. Then you can hire the handicapped—all the other sober alcoholics. It's fun to watch them work!

# XIV

# New Men

# in Your Life

MEN MAY have been the cause or at the least the catalyst in many of your problems. Now that you are slowly working your way out of alcoholism, one day at a time, men can continue to be a problem. The first thing you have to do is meet them if you are single—and meet them on your own terms—without a drink in your hand or in your mind.

One of the best places in the world to meet men is at an A.A. meeting. Many A.A. men are married, but many didn't have time for that sort of frivolity; it interfered with their drinking. They are at these meetings in great numbers, striving, like you, to get and stay sober. The mutual bond of suffering and hope is a powerful one, not a bad basis at all on which to found a mature relationship.

Another great place to meet men is in your therapy session, if you are going to one. Again, you will have the mutual-problem solving situation, the case of mutual help. You will discover that alcoholics have few secrets from each other, that many of them came from similar backgrounds and that they have gone through similar kinds of hell. There is something rather wonderful about coming out of the dark woods together, groping, perhaps, but constantly pushing forward.

Men who have suffered from an alcoholic problem are probably easier to date at the beginning of sobriety than men who don't know anything about it. They are more understanding, more considerate, more aware of you and your problems. And for you, whose looks and personality are just beginning to re-emerge, that's a wonderful kind of situation in which to find yourself.

Still, when you are on your own two feet, you are going to meet other kinds of men—not the men you met in bars or at drunken orgies; that life is no longer for you. But the guys in your office, at your school, at your country club, in your hospital or on your job. How do you manage with them?

Remember: the only date who will be upset if you don't drink is one who has the problem himself. The other may think it a bit odd at first, but soon he won't even notice it. Besides, you are such an inexpensive girl to take out to dinner; the tabs are so much smaller when there are only his drinks on them.

In the beginning being alone with men who drink, even a bit, may make you nervous. You will soon outgrow this as you begin to grow up. There are lots of little tricks you can use. If he's taking you out to dinner, don't go for the cocktail hour; drink tonic or bitter lemon—so long as you have a glass in front of you, most people won't even notice what you're drinking—increase your knowledge of the world and what's in it; if you make your small talk interesting and informative, instead of trite and banal, your date will never notice whether you are drinking or not. No man likes a drunken woman; he'd much rather have you this way.

You will be invited to cocktail parties; you cannot refuse all these invitations. Probably the first thing you will notice is how extremely dull and boring they are. There is nothing more uninspiring than a large horde of people who don't know or care about each other gathered in a room that is too small, eating soggy canapes, drinking too much, getting too loud, and merely occupying floor space in order to be seen. Your first reaction, after the initial shock of the din and stupidity wears off, is sheer boredom. Your second reaction may be surprise: There are a lot of women—men too—present who are not drinking at all. These are the ones to watch; they usually leave early to go to dinner or because they have to be up early in the morning. They can be the most attractive and smartest people present. Just nurse your tonic; every one will think there is gin or vodka in it, and no one will be the wiser.

When the going gets rough, get out. It always helps to have some place to go fairly soon after one of these parties, even if it's home to wash your hair. You'll never regret leaving early. Above all, don't look scared or out of place or blab about your problem. Newly sober people have a great tendency to talk too much, especially about their sobriety. Keep your mouth shut; you will be the only one who is. Wear your most smashing clothes; this is no time for second best, and you won't spill anything on them when you're sober.

You will be invited to business lunches. It is tremendously easy not to drink at a business lunch. All you have to do is murmur girlishly about your figure and your weight problem, or about your having to dash around and do so much work this afternoon you couldn't possibly drink and get befuddled, or about your allergy. No one will question an allergy; it's a super way out—and it's so chic. And you *are* allergic—to alcohol. Certainly you don't have to drink if you are lunching with the girls; if they are your friends, they know, and if they're not, they are too interested in themselves to care about you. Your clothes and your men are much more important to them than your drinking habits. They will merely wonder how come you look so great now.

Dinners are bit more difficult than luncheons. If you are at a formal party and wine is poured, you have two alternatives: Let them pour it into your glass and leave it there, untouched, or tell your host or hostess that you just don't care for any. Few people with manners will insist; the others you shouldn't care about. Or you can give your date your wine; he'll be grateful.

If you are entertaining the client and he wonders why you don't drink along with him; tell him: Tell him you enjoy his company so much you just want to hear him talk, not clog your mind with alcohol. Men are still suckers for this kind of thing, even if they are presidents of their own giant corporations. Tell him you never drink in the middle of the week; it hinders your work. Or tell him you never drink on weekends; that's your exercise and health food time. Tell him anything once; if you are bright and witty and charming enough, he won't ask again. And this is far better than getting drunk, passing out, or, worse yet, telling him off—which you did frequently in the past.

When you travel, not drinking can be a problem. You think you are the only one at the convention or in the resident buying office, who isn't drinking, right?

You couldn't be more wrong. Lots of people aren't drinking; you just never saw them before. Find some of them and make friends; you might like them. It is, perhaps, better not to travel much in the very beginning of your sobriety. You should stay near home base for a while—where you can get help if you need it. Early in the sobriety game, your doctor shouldn't be more than a dime phone call away. However, if you must travel, you will be happy to know that Alcoholics Anonymous has branches in every city, town, village, and hamlet in this country, and in most large cities abroad. They are listed in the phone book. If you are alone in a hotel room and craving a drink, look them up and go to their meeting. They will be delighted to see a fresh face and will welcome you. They may show you around the city, too, or help you in your business. It's like having a built-in family everywhere in the world.

If you are traveling for pleasure and are newly sober, try not to go alone. Go with a good friend or understanding relative; it's much easier. You may have trouble in certain foreign lands when you refuse their native drink; but, I ask you, is it better to be considered a boorish American or a drunken slob? Just ask for bitter lemon or bottled water and look mysterious if any attractive man looks perplexed. Tell him you're traveling for your health and your doctor absolutely forbids alcohol. You certainly aren't lying!

Do not, under any circumstances, fall for the first man who shows more than a passing interest in you. You are on the rebound, from a life of torture and immaturity, perhaps even from one bad marriage. You are like a little girl on her first date; do not flip for the first joker who knows enough to light your cigarette and hold your coat. You know this man is different; maybe he is, but let him prove it. You do not have to get married the first week you are sober, or the first month—or the first year. Anyway, you are probably a lot more interested in him than he is in you. But, do remember you are extremely vulnerable; do not hold your heart or your body out to the first man who asks for it. You will surely regret it later as you grow in sobriety and maturity. Or you will get drunk when he drops you. You won't be the first girl who did.

However, should you meet a really decent man— there are some and time is your best judge—do you tell him about your drinking problem? If you have gone out with him for some time and the sober people you like like him and it is beginning to look serious, the answer is yes. Then, and only then. If you blurt out your drinking story to every man you meet, you will soon get the reputation of being a congenital idiot, a neurotic mess, or an easy target. You are none of these things; why let a man think so? Chances are the man you are serious about will not be surprised when you tell him. He may have suspected something all along and have been waiting for you to discuss it. If he reacts badly, as certain autocratic, mother-dominated types have been known to do, get rid of him fast—even if he is rich. He will make your life a living hell; and he will never let you forget your past indiscretions. Perhaps he will even go so far as to have your past checked out. You don't need him; he's just looking for an outlet for his own neuroses. A real man, a true man, a gentleman, in the full sense of the word, won't give a damn. Except to marvel at your ability to stay sober (and you'd better stay sober if you want to keep him) and to admire you for having gone through what you have and come out of it so well. This is the man for you.

136

If he had a drinking problem and solved it, the two of you are going to have a lot to talk about and enjoy and look forward to.

The most important thing, if and when you decide to get married, is that you are sober enough to know what you are doing, sober enough to accept the responsibilities of marriage, sober enough to be able to withstand its normal pitfalls without resorting to a drink. You must know that your sobriety is the most important thing in your life. Everything else—everything else—is incidental. If you are not sober, nothing else matters. Soon you will revert to your old bad habits, your old miseries, your old problems. And everything you have achieved will be gone; perhaps never to be regained. Sobriety first, marriage and career and family second. If you choose the A.A. route to sobriety there are certain things you should know. In A.A. there are twelve steps. The twelfth step concerns helping other alcoholics to achieve sobriety. As they say in A.A.: men twelfth step men; women twelfth step women. If you go to A.A. and follow members suggestions, you most probably will have a "sponsor." It should be a woman. If she is a good A.A., she will steer you correctly with your problems and help you avoid the traps you can fall into. Two of these concern men: normal men and homosexuals.

About ninety percent of the men in A.A. are great. If they are married, they are concerned with preserving their marriages. If they are single and on the lookout, they are good men, struggling to overcome their problems and to grow up. But there are, as in any other society, a small group of men on the make. Any reasonably attractive woman coming into the program is fair game. Because you are newly sober, you are not thinking as well as you will be when your sobriety grows. You may fall for one of these jokers—and regret it all the days of your life. This is no time for you to think for yourself. Clear thinking is not yet your forte. Rely on the women in the group. They are not vicious, not bitchy, and they will tell you the truth. They know that if you become entangled with one of these men, you will most likely get drunk again. They will help you prevent this. Choose for your friends in A.A. people who have been sober for a good length of time. They know what it's all about; they will steer you correctly.

Also in A.A., especially in the large urban groups, there is a large number of homosexuals. Many of them are alcoholics, striving to achieve sobriety. But there are some who attend meetings to encounter other homosexuals. Try and avoid joining a primarily homosexual group. Do not fall into the trap of being flattered by their attentions; you are merely their smoke screen. Then, too, there are those very sad cases, the men who don't know what they are or who they are, whether they are attracted to men or women. If you choose one of these to be your marriage partner, you are really headed for trouble. Again, time is the answer, time plus reliance on the older members of the group who know more than you do.

If you succeed in avoiding a deeply disturbed man and succeed in avoiding the homosexual—female as well as male—your chances of choosing a fine marriage partner are good. Do not choose a man who is presently married—even if he is about to be divorced or has been separated for twenty years. He may be a Catholic who has no intention of re-marrying and is using the Church as an excuse. He may be using you. Girls who are not alcoholic, not addicted to pills have trouble enough with married men. You are in no shape at all to cope with this problem. There are plenty of other men, especially these days when men are learning about A.A. at younger and younger ages.

Let us say you have found the ideal man. And your present ideal may be a far different thing than it was when you were drinking. You may find a short, bald, fat gentlemen of sixty who will make the world's greatest husband, or a young struggling artist of twenty-five who will succeed in life with your help. Don't look for beauty of face and body; look for gentleness, understanding, and character. You will find them, even if you have to wait.

You get married. You will probably have the greatest marriage on record, a marriage beyond your wildest dreams. I have met more truly happily married couples in A.A. than I have ever seen anywhere before or since. They know the problems life can bring; they face them together. When an A.A. wife looks over her shoulder for help, her husband is there—not off with his secretary or his job.

A.A. men make truly superb fathers, if they practice A.A. principles. They are not away when their children need them; they know how to guide, lead, and advise. They are men who have almost been destroyed, who have lost it all, and who often have come back to even greater heights. They are men of character and wisdom. Above all, they are men, not little boys. And they almost invariably have a splendid sense of humor. What more can you ask from a marriage partner?

If you choose for a life partner a man who is a nonalcoholic, your road may be a bit different, not neces-

sarily more difficult, just different. You must be sure
that he understands your problem, that at some future
date he is not going to urge you to have just "one" with
him. You must always remember there is no such thing
as just one for you.

There are many problems in being an alcoholic, not
all of which disappear when you stop drinking. You
will have to work on your resentments and hostilities
every day of your life. You will have to be and remain
honest with yourself, otherwise, your sobriety is in
constant jeopardy. You must be sure enough of yourself
and your husband to know whether or not you will
resent his drinking, even if it is only one before dinner.
You have to be sure enough of him to know whether he
will resent or be jealous of time spent in therapy or at
your A.A. meetings. Will he dislike your constant attendance at meetings, your volunteer work on the part
of other alcoholics, perhaps your serving on alcoholic
committees? If he does, will you give them up for his
sake? If you do, will you remain sober?

You will not have his kind of release when something
goes wrong. You cannot go out and tie one on with the
girls—or the boys. You cannot take sleeping pills to
help you through the night or tranquilizers to see you
through your bad days. Your neuroses may manifest
themselves in a variety of immature ways: You may
become withdrawn and resentful; you may become
overly ambitious; you may try to do too much work;
you may not be able to pace yourself. You may try to be
all things to one man. But you must not do this; if you
try, you will drink. It isn't always easy to throw dinner
parties for your husband's family or boss and be the
only one present not drinking. If he travels on business
a great deal, and you're alone and not attending A.A.

meetings because he doesn't want you to, what are you going to do with your time? Drink?

Above all, you cannot be a Pollyanna. You cannot be filled with such sweetness and light at all times that he wishes he could punch you in the jaw. You cannot bend over backward to show him you don't mind his drinking. If you mind it, say so—once in a while. Maybe he drinks too much and needs help. If he resents your criticism, think twice about it.

There are many men who are non-alcoholics who have other problems and neuroses. Maybe at one extreme, he is a psychopath, a classic clinical case. Maybe at the other extreme, he won't hang up his clothes. You cannot let his irritating little mannerisms get to you; you must watch yourself at all times. Resentment breeds bad thinking; bad thinking breeds drinking.

It takes a very understanding and mature man to marry an arrested alcoholic. There are such men; just be sure you find one. Be sure before you marry him that he knows what the problems you two will encounter are. Take him to your psychiatrist and let him talk to him; or take him to an A.A. meeting and let him hear for himself. Don't assume he knows. How could he? If he is still willing to take you on, be grateful and marry him. Work hard at creating a good marriage; fulfill yourself and stay sober.

If you are already married and manage to get sober, you have an entirely different set of problems. Unless you are extremely lucky, or have children for whose sake your husband stayed around, chances are he left long ago. He listened to your promises to sober up just as long as he could, then he finally took off. And who can blame him? Men just have very little sticking power

141

when it comes to alcoholic wives. Accept it as a fact of life: Men don't stick, women most times do. There are exceptions, of course. Some men stay with alcoholic wives because they were once alcoholic themselves and feel they owe this to them—you'd be amazed at the number of women who take to drink when their husbands get sober. She cannot forgive him; she resents his growing sobriety and ability to take over once more as the head of the household; she resents his increasing authority over the children; she resents losing her "power." If he spends too much time at A.A. meetings, she feels neglected and out of it; her bitterness and hostility grow. She gives him a dose of his own medicine. Needless to say, this is not very bright. No matter how drunk and mean and far down the scale a man went, he is not going to hang around forever with a sadistic, vengeful wife. If he does, he may go back to drinking himself.

Some men stay with alcoholic wives because they are decent, honorable, ever hopeful men who try to help the women they love. These are few and far between. Some men stay for the sake of the children; some men stay because their wives have the money and they've become accustomed to a way of life they don't earn; some men stay because they are masochists and enjoy it. Some men stay because they are afraid of what their wives will do to themselves: suicide, fire, vehicular homicide. But most men go. If your husband has departed, it may have been the shock you needed to make you sober up! He should have done it long ago!

The first thing you must decide is whether or not you want him back. Think about this carefully; perhaps your incompatibility started you drinking in the first place. Just because you are no longer drinking doesn't mean a bad marriage is going to become a good one. It may be better; chances are it will not. If your husband was long-suffering and decent, and you still love him, you should try to reconcile with him. First making sure, of course, that he is not involved with another woman and totally devoid of any tender sentiment for you. If he has divorced you and remarried, then that's that. Chalk it up to experience; don't be resentful. You did it to yourself; now you owe yourself a new life. Go out and get it and don't look back. "What might have been" makes for quick and easy drinking.

The first thing you must do if you want your husband back is to let him know you are no longer drinking and that this time you mean it. He will not be easily convinced. If you can, get him to go with you to your doctor; get him to go with you to your A.A. meetings. Let him learn and understand about the disease for himself. Do not expect him to leap into your arms with joy the first time he sees you sober. You have kicked him once too often for him not to cringe. You have cut him to ribbons emotionally; it may take him a long time to work his way out of the mess. But time *is* on your side. If he sees you are constantly sober, day after day, if he realizes you are *really* trying to work on yourself, most likely he will want to help you. Remember: Sobriety alone is not your total goal. You must try for a new way of life, devoid of self-hatred and resentment. It is much easier if you have a man at your side who is willing to try along with you. If you do, thank God for him and keep going.

His friends may be surprised if he returns to you. They may whisper behind your back; snide remarks will be directed over your head quite often. Shut your ears and your mouth; you deserve them. If you stay

143

sober and work on yourself, they will soon stop. All that matters is *you*, not them. They don't care if you resent them; they may even enjoy it. All it will do for you is move you one step nearer the bar.

Start to improve your looks. If you are fat and bloated, don't see your husband until you have lost weight. Act as if he were courting you all over again.

After the last time he saw you, maybe in a straight-jacket in a hospital ward, he will probably be so shocked and delighted at the change in you, he could be eager to see what makes you tick. If you haven't cooked a decent meal for him in years get moving. It's part of your job. Feel like a girl again, even if you are sixty. If you are shy about discussing your problems with your husband, that's all right, too. A little girlish shyness never hurt any man-woman relationship, so long as you don't cover it up with defensive cynicism. If you truly still love your husband, you will know what to do. If you don't, you should know enough to get out.

Quite often, when a girl sobers up and her husband is still around, she may discover to her horror that she can't stand him. It is only fair and honorable to yourself and him to let him go. Don't keep him around for a meal ticket; get out and earn your own. It's the only way you will enjoy your sobriety; it may be the only way you will keep it.

Sober now, you are on extremely ticklish ground with your children, if you have them. Your first and most overwhelming desire will be to make up to them in spades for what you have done to them in the past. One word of warning: DON'T!

As many children are ruined by the permissiveness

and over-compensation of their arrested alcoholic mothers as were ruined by the drinking. Your children will be confused, resentful of you, or totally unable to relate to you at all. But they are also smart! If the little darlings discover that in mother's new phase they can get anything and everything they want, rest assured they will do so.

There really is no telling what damage your drinking may have done to your children. You can only hope and pray that you have not ruined them for life. If you had a strong and decent husband, your chances are good. If you were both alcoholic, your chances are very bad. Yet children are amazingly resilient; they are strong. If they manifest neurotic symptoms, take them to a child psychologist right away. If you cannot afford one, talk to your own doctor about getting help for them or go to a child guidance clinic. Help, professional help, is available—and it is important.

But the worst thing you can do is to over-indulge the children. If they are old enough, perhaps you can talk to them. You may be able to explain to them about your disease; they may understand very well and not resent you so much. Again, if they are old enough, take them to an A.A. meeting with you or send them to an Ala-Teen meeting. There, children of alcoholics with similar problems help each other in a kind of mutual therapy. You might suggest to your husband that he go to Ala-Non, which is a group of relatives and friends of drinking and arrested alcoholics who meet to help alcoholics and themselves. It *always* helps to know there are others in the same boat!

If your children are young, no permanent damage may have been done. But you cannot worm yourself

145

back into their shattered affections overnight, or by buying them everything in the department store. Your children and you will have to grope slowly to a mutual understanding, trust, and respect. Love most likely will emerge when they realize you are trying. They may become your best friends, your staunchest allies. It will be a joy for them to be able to bring their friends home again without worrying whether or not Mommy is laid out cold on the living-room floor.

You should go and see their teachers. You may have to explain to them what has happened to you and what you are doing about it. If your children's teacher recommends special help or a special school, get it. Your children are your most important responsibility; they deserve whatever you can do for them—*in a rational way*.

But your children still need discipline; perhaps they need it more than ever. This does not mean you start screaming at them or punishing them for minor infractions of household rules. After all, they have been on their own quite a bit and they will resent anything like this coming from you.

But, mainly because they are confused, nervous, and overwrought, they need a firm hand on the tiller. They need to know the meaning of authority, but authority which is earned, not arbitrarily and dictatorially assumed. Do not give your daughters every dress they clamor for; do not feel you must buy your son a car. Above all, do not feel you must social climb on their account because they have been so ashamed of you in the past. Think a minute. Are you social climbing for them or for yourself?

Answer their questions fairly and as honestly as you can. Try not to resent their hostility toward you. Try to teach them about the good things in life; try to provide a good example. If you don't, you are breeding people who will go through the same things you have just been through.

Midge and Jim Tobin were both alcoholics. They both had been drinking hard and long. He sobered up before she did, after leaving her to try and regain his sobriety. Eventually, after a bad bout with pills and refusing to accept the fact that she was alcoholic, she too became sober. They were separated for about a year after she stopped drinking, but finally got together to try and patch up their marriage.

They had two children, both girls. The older girl, though scarred by her parents' alcoholism, was just old enough to understand. She realized it was a disease, and she realized both her parents were trying their best. But the younger girl, Tracy, a teenager, reacted badly. She had run away from home three times when her parents were still drinking, and had been returned each time by the police. She had been in a private school, but was asked to leave. Her parents thought that upon their achievement of sobriety Tracy would eventually understand and be all right. But such was not the case.

Tracy went from school to school. She ran away from all of them. Her mother sent her to a child psychologist; she absolutely refused to co-operate with him or to keep going to him. She was then put into a remedial school in a northeastern state. There she got involved with girls who knew a lot more than she. She tried marijuana, drugs, LSD, and any other form of escape she could get her hands on. She disappeared on weekends with boys, often having to be returned by the police. Finally, even this last school called her parents and told them they could do nothing for her. By now she was eighteen.

Her father was willing to give up; he had had pastoral counseling and was becoming resigned. But her mother would not give up. Midge nearly drove herself insane with worry and fear. Tracy moved across the country away from her parents' home; they only heard from her when she needed money. Her mother contacted friends, ministers, doctors, psychologists—all in vain.

Tracy was picked up on a narcotics charge and sent to prison. Her mother went to see her; but she refused to see her mother. Finally, as the prison doors clanged shut, Midge, too, knew Tracy was lost to her forever. Tracy would have to find her own way in life, if, indeed, she ever could.

Doctors told Midge that Tracy was a psychopath; they told her to go home and pick up the threads of her life—and those of her husband and her other daughter, whom she had sadly neglected once more. Today, Midge and Jim are reasonably happy. Their older daughter is well-married and happy. They haven't heard from Tracy in five years; they don't even know where she is.

Permissiveness and over-compensation are not the answers to regaining your children's love and affection. Growing up on your part, meeting problems maturely and without rancor are the answers. If one of your children turns out badly and you have tried everything you possibly can—psychology, special schools, love and affection, and so on—then you will simply have to face it and go on living. One of the hardest things a mother can ever face is the fact that a child of hers has turned

148

out badly, and it is partly her fault. But face it you must; you must go on. You, too, have a life to live and self-excoriation will not help you live it. Do the best you can; if your best is not good enough, shut the door. That is all you can do.

# X V

# Red Alerts

# for the Newly Sober

THE NEWLY sober, the newly non-addicted are, in many ways, just like children. They become as addicted to sobriety as they had been to alcoholism and pill addiction. This, essentially, is good, but there are dangers.

You must watch out that you don't become a "kook" about your sobriety. It's very easy and it's often done, especially by people who had achieved little or nothing before or during their drinking and who now become important by virtue of their recovery from alcoholism. Like the Prodigal Son, you may be greeted by family, friends, therapists, doctors, fellow A.A.'s, employers, and husbands with great joy. You may become self-important, full of your own abilities. Don't! You didn't become sober by yourself and you're not going to stay that way by yourself.

The first mistake you will probably perpetrate on the innocent around you when you sober up is talking of nothing else but your sobriety. For those who were devastated by your drinking, this is splendid—for a while. But eventually it begins to pall even on them. You will discover all kinds of things about yourself: Why you drank, how you drank, what was wrong with you, how courageous you are to overcome these difficulties, how you can stay sober, and so forth. And you will babble on and on and on. You will become a first-class bore. Talky women are boring to begin with; when they talk on only one subject, themselves, they are to be avoided. And when your friends begin to avoid you because you are such a bore, you will once again become hostile and resentful. You may once again begin to drink. This is the *only* way you can recapture their attention. The way to avoid this vicious circle is to keep your ears open and your mouth shut. There are many people around who know a great deal more than you do; they have been through more than you. Listen to them and learn. Stop talking!

The second mistake you can make is to shut out most or all other activities and interests in your life save your doctor, your therapist, or your A.A. friends and their activities. In the very beginning, of course, you won't be capable of much outside activity. You must get sober first, and you must walk along a bit on the path to maturity. But as you come out of the haze, the fog, the doubts, the guilts, and the self-hatreds your world should expand. If it doesn't, there is something basically wrong with you. If you see only other ex-alcoholics and depend on them for support, if you cannot function in the world around you without constant attention from a doctor, if you read only books and treatises on alcoholism and pills, if your activities are girdled completely by A.A. meetings, then you need help and you need it quickly. You are still a small, scared little girl craving attention, dependent and lacking in courage. You will become boring and bored. Once the attention from people turns to someone else who needs help, you may return to drinking or to your pill bottle. At best, if you don't drink, you will not learn to grow up, to stand on your own. You will live a narrow, constricted, tortured life, with few interests and fewer friends. You will go on being afraid of everyone and everything. Psychiatry, Alcoholics Anonymous, therapy, and religion should not be used as eternal crutches. They will help you get and stay sober. But like everything else in life, the rest is up to you.

The third mistake is usually made by the married women. They have discovered a new outlet for their problems. It is called "Their Sobriety!" Their husbands and children are supposed to bow down to this; one mustn't get Mother upset, she may drink. Meals are geared to her attendance at A.A. meetings. She cannot go with her husband to office parties; she may drink. Her friends are other ex-drunks; her life is centered around her problems. Unless your husband is the most extraordinary man alive, he will fast become disgusted with this kind of living. He would like to have someone else to talk to besides a living martyr. And he will find someone. It had better be you.

Your children have their own problems; they are not all that fired up about yours all the time. Your family will slowly begin to resent your sobriety as much as they resented your drinking. And, if your husband is confused enough, he may encourage your return to it.

Your medical and psychiatric bills may not make him too happy either. You expect to be treated like a fragile doll, without having earned it. Just because you are sober, you expect the sun to rise and set only for you. Well, it won't. And the sooner you learn it won't, the better off you will be.

How do you avoid all these pitfalls? You avoid them basically by growing up. This will, of course, take time, maybe lots of time. But you should and must strive toward maturity. You must learn to accept responsibility; you must learn not to react hysterically or childishly to everything that upsets you; you must learn, above all, to care for others; you must learn that you are not the center of the universe; you must learn to give wholly and unstintingly of yourself. This way lies happiness, growth, maturity, and emotional stability. Frustration, morbidity, and doom belong to the selfish; life, health, and humor belong to the truly giving. It's an old cliché; but it's true. And it is especially true and important for an alcoholic, because what lies ahead for you is worse than what lies ahead for most people— self-destruction, hospitals, and death.

You will begin to learn to live all over again by doing what you are told by your doctor, your therapist, your A.A. "sponsor." In the beginning let other, wiser people make your decisions for you. But as your personality emerges—bruised and battered perhaps, but your very own—feed and nourish it. Be good to yourself, but never at the expense of others. Take care of yourself physically. Start to read: the newspapers—the war news, the society page, the women's page, the sports page. You have been missing a lot! Read books— novels, books on music, gardening, history, biography. Go to concerts and the theater if you can. Take an honest interest in your job, if you have one; don't slough it off; don't let it run you into the ground. Travel, if you can afford it. Fix up your home the way you would like it to be. It doesn't have to be expensive so long as you like it. Don't constantly try to outdo your neighbors. That way lies frustration.

Don't resent people's comments about you; maybe they are deserved. See as many of your friends as you can, especially those who are vitally alive and interesting. Do not restrict your friendships to ex-drunks! Make new friends—where you work, where you play. Don't fall for every new fad or movement around; don't seek refuge or solace or life itself in quack religions, faddish new drugs, or doctors with new treatments for youth and beauty. Have a few convictions and stick by them. Work from the inside out. Do not be influenced by every new person you meet; have an entity of your own.

Everything, in spite of what you read, is not relative. Do not throw yourself frantically into new and unproven causes. Develop a sense of what is right and what is wrong for you. Develop a sense of judgment, a sense of propriety for your life. Be curious, but not nosy. Do not gossip. Give help when and where you can to those who *really* need it; don't waste your time, energy, and money on the world's parasites. Devote it, instead, to the man who loves you or the people who deserve your love. Do not be afraid to be alone, physically or emotionally. We are all alone. Don't feel you must fill every waking minute with fruitless activity. Develop a sense of serenity, a sense of courage, and a sense of justice. Do not be cynical or overawed. Learn, above all else to love. Not only is this good advice for alcoholics but it is an ideal all mature people should strive toward.

# XVI

# Escaping

# from Pills

CRITIC Leslie Fiedler said recently that the U.S. is changing from a "whiskey culture to a drug culture." And this may very well be true. Well over half of the alcoholics who seek help and release from liquor today are also addicted to pills and drugs, in one form or another. Escaping from them, from their insidious hold over you is more difficult than escaping from alcohol; escaping from the combination is dreadfully difficult and painful. But is can be done.

A pill is the same as a drink to an alcoholic. If you take one, you may soon take the other. It is a fact, proven by thousands of arrested alcoholics; don't think it can't happen to you. You use pills the way you use liquor—for escape, from tension, frustration, hopelessness, fear, and anxiety. You use pills as a crutch. When you learn, as you must, to face the realities of life on your own two feet, when you have grown up, you will not need pills.

How do you stop taking pills, if you are addicted? The first thing you must do is learn to be honest with yourself. You must learn that life was not always meant to be easy; it is not nirvana, nor is it an earthly paradise. You create a "false paradise" for yourself with pills. You are running away. But this false paradise never lasts; you need more and more pills to create it and live in it. If you take enough pills, you will soon die in it.

If you are addicted, go at once to your doctor and tell him the truth. If you don't have a doctor, call your nearest out-patient psychiatric clinic and ask them for help. Your doctor, whether he is a general practioner or a psychiatrist, should know, and most likely does know by now, the dangers of addictive drugs. Doctors who are aware and have a knowledge of alcoholism will know that some alcoholics can become addicted even to aspirin. If your doctor doesn't respond to what you are talking about get another doctor quickly. Do not kid yourself because your doctor says you are not dependent on these drugs. You may be an addictive personality. He may not know it; but he is not the one who may die. Only you know the truth; only you can do something about it.

Withdrawal from tranquilizers and barbiturates is an inferno. Whichever circle of hell it may be for you depends on how addicted you are. A friend of mine did a TV show at the public health hospital in Lexington. He came away shaken and extremely disturbed. He felt the withdrawal from barbiturates was equally as painful, if not more so, than the withdrawal from drugs.

Pill addiction is a "sneaky" disease. Pills are so easy to get, so easy to take, so easy to hide. They are far more insidious than liquor because of this. There is no sour gin smell on your breath from pills; in the beginning you do not stagger or fall down. You will not be arrested for drunken driving or tossed in jail for being a vagrant. Society does not scorn you for your weakness; society does not know.

At first you may take pills to recover from your hangovers. That is the way most alcoholics begin. The release is wonderful: the shakes are stopped, the stomach butterflies are stopped, the fears go away—so do the remorse, the guilt, and the sense of reality. How marvelous for you! Soon, as with alcohol, your body and mind crave more and more pills; one will no longer do the trick. You will be taking benzedrine to get going in the morning, tranquilizers to keep calm during the day, and barbiturates to sleep at night. Whether or not you couple this with liquor, soon you will be on the world's most treacherous merry-go-round. You will take a pill to avoid an office crisis, a scrap at home, a sleepless night. You cannot allow yourself to feel depressed; you take a pill. At this stage you cannot get dressed in the morning without a pill; you cannot get through the day without a whole supply. Your behavior becomes erratic; your memory ceases to function. You don't know whom you called or when; you don't remember whom you invited to dinner or why. Soon you will go out of your mind. You will wind up in a hospital in a straight-jacket, screaming. Or you will, perhaps unknowingly, take the one pill too many, and you will die.

If you are hooked, but still able to function a little, get medical help immediately. Your doctor will know what withdrawal means; he will be able to ease the physical torments for you. If you are badly addicted, he may recommend that you go to a hospital or sanitarium for treatment. Make sure it is one that does not treat pill addiction lightly. Call the National Council on Alcoholism, the American Medical Association, or Alcoholics Anonymous for recommendations. These organizations are all listed in your phone book. If you have no funds for rehabilitation, ask your local social welfare office to recommend you to a state hospital. Some state hospitals are far more advanced in the treatment of addiction than are private sanitariums.

Even with the best withdrawal treatment, the best substitute non-addictive drugs, there will be some physical discomfort. It is still a law of nature that what goes up must come down. Your nerves, your body, your organs will react. Your craving may be enormous; you must fight it—*if* you want to survive. Try and feel that you are headed toward a new life, that good things are going to happen to you—and remember that many good things in life begin with sacrifice and pain. In this case the game, your life, is well worth the candle.

A woman who runs an excellent sanitarium in the State of New Jersey once told me that it is difficult to get an addict off pills once; to do it twice is almost impossible. Once you are off them, remember every day of your life, every waking moment that you crave a pill, the agony of withdrawal. Don't recall how you felt when you took pills; remember how you felt when you could no longer get them. It will help keep you away from pills in the beginning.

Medical and, often, psychiatric and psychological help probably will be needed so that you can quit. Supportive therapy—whether from a clergyman, a public-health nurse, a doctor, or Alcoholics Anonymous—is needed to stay off pills. Your chances of returning to pills are tripled without continuing help. And you cannot substitute the oral panacea of non-addictive drugs or over-the-counter non-prescription tablets forever either. You are merely reducing the size of your crutch, not throwing it away. Again, as with alcohol, these particular drugs may only continue and increase your habit pattern to the point where you return to your own lethal little pill bottle.

What you need is a completely new way of life—new habit patterns, new thinking patterns, new emotional reactions, new raw courage. No one ever said it was easy. But it has been done by thousands before you, and their experiences are available to help you.

Marilyn came from a small town; ever since she could talk, she had wanted to be an actress. After graduating from high school she got a job as a band singer and took acting lessons everywhere and every time she could. She toured all over the country; she never stopped working. She learned to drink with the musicians; from them she also learned the "help" pills could give her to avoid hangovers and missed performances. She was doing very well with national tours when she was offered a Broadway acting part. She accepted and became almost an overnight success. With the advent of television, she became famous all over the country. She decreased her drinking, but stepped up her consumption of pills "to keep going."

Soon she began to miss rehearsals; her agent and her family protected her. Charges for a car accident for which she was responsible were dismissed for lack of evidence; no one could smell liquor on her breath. Soon she missed a performance. She had never done this before; she was shocked. She signed herself into a private sanitarium for treatment; she stopped drinking and taking pills—for a time.

Again, her career assumed gigantically successful proportions. She was always busy, always in great demand. When she was tired, she took a drink. She was soon hooked once more. Fortunately, her TV shows had already all been taped because it was holiday time. She disappeared; her sister found her on Christmas morning in a small, cheap hotel.

She went to her doctor; again she stopped drinking. But she was once more taking pills, which she did not tell him about. The same old routine occurred—missed rehearsals, missed performances, missing Marilyn. Her sister persuaded her to go to an excellent hospital which knew about pill addiction. She remained there for five months. She came out and went to California to do a movie. There, she once more started on benzedrine and phenobarbitol.

This time it was a world-famous hospital for three months. Her reputation for unreliability had now spread; she was not quite so avidly sought after. Her agent found her another TV show, in which she is now rehearsing. At this point she is drinking again and has once more been heard asking around town where she can obtain pills. Her prognosis is not good; perhaps she has been too sheltered and protected. Perhaps she must lose nearly everything before she learns that "one pill is too many; a hundred is not enough."

One of the more interesting sidelights to pill addiction, as in alcohol addiction, is that the smartest people often fall the hardest. The brainy bright girls of this world—always on the go, never missing anything, always "with it," switched on—these are the ones who take to pills. They take them to keep going, to get going, and to stop going. They figure addiction can never happen to them; they are too smart. They know the problems, pitfalls, and evils involved. They lie to their parents, to their doctors, to their friends, and most of all to themselves about how much and what kind of pills they are consuming. And, inevitably, their systems crave more and stronger medication. Inevitably, they are caught.

Intellectual knowledge is *not* enough! You can have a mind like a computer and still get hooked on pills or, worse yet, on the narcotics, LSD, or other chemical substitutions for living. Along with the intellect, you must develop a sense of emotional balance. Your parents and grandparents would have called it common sense. If your life is such that you feel a need for pills; if you are constantly overtired, bored, nervous, fearful, unself-confident; if you are often hungover; if your job or your home life demands so much of you that you cannot function without pills then you must go to work at once on *you!* You must change you.

If necessary, you must give up what is driving you to chemical suicide, whether it is the pursuit of success, money, power, a man, or a new religion. If it is fear, anxiety, or failure—or all three—that is driving you to seek solace in pills, to push away the outside world, find out why you are afraid. Putting it off with phony solutions won't take care of your problems. Pills, sought as an escape, will never solve your problems. Like alcohol, pills will only make problems worse. Pills may hide problems temporarily; they may allow you to live in a world of cotton wool for a time; they may make reality nonexistent for you for a few hours or a few days. But in the end they will deprive you of even the limited tools

163

for living that you use now to cope with your life and your problems.

Take yourself as rapidly as possible for psychiatric help. Once you have gone through the physical agony of withdrawal, once your physical craving ceases to be a living, breathing, tearing thing inside you, the only way you are going to stay away from pills is with professional and medical help. If you are a member of Alcoholics Anonymous to combat your drinking, the organization may also be able to help you get off pills. The reasons behind your pill addiction are the same as the reasons behind your alcoholism—only pill addiction is more insidious. A pill addict finds it even more difficult to be honest with herself, to face life on its own terms. Alcoholics may at least have had a measure of sociability and gregariousness, as I have described, but pill people are basically sneaky. Good A.A.'s will probably recommend that you get to a competent doctor and that you tell him the truth.

Work with your doctor; don't lie to him. And start to work on yourself. The longest journey begins with the first step. Try to grow up, painful as it may be. Try to tell yourself the truth, even for one hour at a time. Try to fill at least part of your life with something or someone besides yourself. Try to give a little, instead of always grabbing. Life is not easy, not for anyone. Try to remember everyone doesn't run away. Join the stickers. Face up—a little bit at a time. It will grow easier as you go along. This is the road to sanity, to health. You won't make it with a little pill hidden in a secret compartment against emergencies. You *will* make it if you try—one day at a time—to grow up.

# XVII

# The Point

# of No Return

Do WOMEN, once they have recovered from alcoholism and pill addiction, return to them? Yes, believe it or not, they do! A non-addict, a non-alcoholic cannot possibly believe this. How, they say, can anyone who has gone through the living hell of hangovers, of withdrawal, of degradation and disgrace even consider returning to alcohol or pills? How?

It is the very nature of the disease; the sneaky, lying, phony, vicious nature of the disease itself. Because this disease is not merely physical, because it is also mental and moral and spiritual, the physical horrors are soon forgotten. One of the truly great advantages of A.A. is the therapeutic value of telling one's story. It reminds you, every time you speak of what has happened to you, of what has gone before; you cannot forget. Even if your story helps no one else listening to you, even if no one else in the room identifies with you, it helps *you* to speak. It is one of the original ideas of man that confession is good for the soul. Whether this confession is to a priest, an analyst, a roomful of alcoholics, or your own doctor, this idea is still true, especially for ex-drunks who tend to forget what the gutter was like once they have put their houses in order.

The return to drinking begins long before you take the actual drink. It begins with fouled-up thinking. It can begin with a small voice deep in the subconscious saying to you: Why not? Maybe you're not really alcoholic after all; maybe you were just going through a difficult period. The seed is planted. It will begin to grow.

Next you begin to lie to yourself; honesty becomes alien to you once more. You begin to feel sorry for yourself again. You are an outcast with the mark of Cain; you cannot drink like other people. You begin to resent people who drink "normally" and well. You begin to avoid A.A. meetings. You begin to avoid your therapist. You begin to lie to those who love you. You begin to plan your drunk—perhaps still only subconsciously. You find yourself, perhaps, back in your old haunts, among your old drinking friends. Your old habit patterns begin to take hold once more. You may still be able to pass the cocktail lounge or the bar or the tray of drinks, but it's getting harder.

Perhaps you begin to think just one tranquilizer won't hurt you. Or something traumatic happens in your life and you feel the only way to survive it is to take a phenobarbitol. This something traumatic may be a death in the family, or it may be the fact that the tailor didn't return your dresses on time for the party.

You begin to resent the people who told you you couldn't drink in the first place. Who are they? What do they know? You start to work yourself up into a rotten mental state. *Or* you think people have turned their attention from you to someone else. Maybe, if you are in Alcoholics Anonymous, some newcomers are getting all the attention. Maybe you aren't the white-hot flash you were a few weeks or a few months ago. Maybe things have simmered down at home or in the office; the heat is off. And your deprived little ego begins to squirm. It whispers to you: All right, if that's the way they feel about it, I'll show them. But you won't show anybody anything except what a child you really are.

So, saying to yourself in your own inimitable, lying manner, "I can have just one," you proceed to your first drink—once again. You may not get drunk right away; you may not even have more than one that first time. Or you may not take more than one phenobarbitol that first day. But what of the next day, and the next? What of next week? If you are addicted, whether it be to pills or alcohol or both, you will very shortly be "hooked" once more. Only this time it will be much, much worse. Because alcoholism is a progressive disease your tolerance to liquor will be the same as if you had never stopped drinking at all. You will get drunk faster and more disastrously than you ever did. But there is one essential difference. You will not enjoy it— ever, ever again. Psychiatry and/or Alcoholics Anonymous will have ruined any pleasure you hope to get from alcohol. There will be no release, no joy, no gregariousness; only guilt, remorse, and shame doubled and trebled. Anxiety will descend upon you as it never did before. You will be back in no time flat to the exact point you were when you decided to stop drinking.

But the fatal question remains: Will you be able to stop this time? How many chances do you expect to be given in life? You had your sobriety, your happiness, your life handed back to you. You threw it away again. Will you regain it once more?

Some people do; some people don't. Intellectually, you know what you have done. You know what you must do to climb back again. But all the emotional balance, all the maturity you achieved has been destroyed. Your old habit patterns are once more established, ingrained more deeply than ever, beckoning you onward to destruction. Control is gone; serenity is gone. Will you make it? I don't know; neither do you. Why chance it?

The way to avoid returning to drinking is to be ever vigilant. This doesn't mean you have to wear sackcloth and ashes and go around shouting about your martyrdom. Far from it. People who act like that are always suspect anyhow. If you are in A.A. go to meetings, keep going to meetings, then go to more meetings. If you are getting bored, go to another group. Do what they tell you; help out; work and speak if you can. If you want and crave their attention, earn it. Don't throw yourself at their feet drunk and asking for pity. Even ex-drunks can get fed up with your act.

If you are in therapy call your doctor or your psychologist and tell him how you feel. Talk to him; he's getting paid to help you. To stop yourself physically from returning to alcohol or pills use your head and your phone. That's all you have to do. If you can't find anyone else to listen to you, try your family. They'd rather listen to you ramble on and on than pick you up out of the gutter. Walk into any parish house or rectory and talk to the clergyman there. Call an out-patient clinic and talk to the attendant on the phone. When you've talked and talked and talked, you very likely will not feel like drinking. Stuff yourself with ice cream, cake, candy—anything to keep from drinking. The craving *will* pass. Do anything not to take that first drink or that first pill. It's the first drink that gets you drunk.

When you have calmed down and can look at yourself rationally, try to be honest with yourself. Some people are congenitally incapable of this. They are very sick indeed and should be in the care of a good psychiatrist. But if you are the common, ordinary, garden-variety drunk, like most other people, take a good hard look at yourself. Where have you gone off the track? Why have you begun to feel sorry for yourself? Why have you allowed your ego to grow so out of proportion once more? Why do you resent other people, many of whom deserve nothing but gratitude from you? In short, who are *you?*

Look around you and count your blessings. If you are depressed, remember two things: depression is selfish, and if you try it will go away. Go out and do something for someone else, maybe for someone you don't even like. It could have a shocking effect on you; you might like it. Give your ego a hard twist by its fat neck and get some humility. If you feel you are totally worthless, you are merely waiting for someone to come along and tell you you are not; you are really great. It's still ego, no matter how you slice it. If you have an inferiority complex, maybe you *are* inferior. You won't get to be superior by drinking—or popping pills.

You *will* get to be a decent, marvelous human being by taking an inventory of your shortcomings—the real ones, not the imagined ones. And, after inventory, start doing something about them. Everyone has shortcomings; you are not alone. Your character defects may be more obvious than other people's; that doesn't mean you can't work on them. You will never be perfect; you

169

would be totally inhuman if you were. All you need ask out of this world is a chance to live in it as a fairly normal, reasonably happy, human being. If you concentrate you can do it—one day at a time.

Yesterday is finished, done. Tomorrow may never come. All anyone has is today. Use it. You will never have today if you hide in a bottle. If you have once made a comeback from alcoholism or pill addiction, don't slide back—for any reason whatsoever. You may have used up all your chances. This time the name on the police blotter's death list may be yours. And, worst of all, now you know it doesn't have to be.

# EPILOGUE

As I have said at the beginning of this book, alcohol is the great leveler, so are pills. As twin crutches in life, they are no respecters of age, sex, station in life, fortune, morality, or appearance.

You are never too young to become an alcoholic. There have been cases reported of girls becoming addicted to alcohol from their very first drink at the age of twelve. Therefore, don't think because you are sixteen or nineteen and can handle your liquor, or because you take your nightly sleeping pill, you are immune to this disease. Age and health may be in your favor; it also may only mean that you drag your albatross around with you longer than you would if you were older. If there is something wrong with the way you drink, no matter how young you are, go and do something about it right now.

Conversely, you are never too young to sober up.

In fact, it is much easier when you are young. You have your whole life ahead of you to do with what you will. You have not destroyed much of your reputation yet; you probably have not lost many jobs or ruined yourself morally or physically. It is easier to stop drinking and taking pills if you are young, too, because they have not yet become life-long habit patterns. The only thing that stands in your way is your probable doubt about being alcoholic. Remember the rule of thumb: If you're worried, you probably have a reason to be. Don't wait; don't destroy your life. Sober up, grow up now—and look forward excitedly to a new, invigorating, rewarding life. And, if you're looking for company, you should know that there are 5,000,000 people in America who shouldn't be drinking either.

You are never too old to be an alcoholic or a pill addict. Ladies, in the true sense of the word, have become addicted at ages ranging from sixty on upward. This age is, perhaps, a lonely time of life or a less busy one. It is easy to start drinking sherry with the "girls" and wind up drinking muscatel by yourself. Many ladies of uncertain age are secret drinkers. Rest assured, they won't be secret drinkers long.

If you are clutching at your lost youth, this is the fastest way to destroy it. If you are afraid to face life, this is the surest way to increase your anxiety. If you are alone, this is the best way to stay lonely. Don't beg your doctor for pills for every little ailment; he may give them to you. You can wind up very sick or dead with these pills. If you feel you have little or nothing to live for, you couldn't be more wrong. Go to Alcoholics Anonymous and find out how much they need you—almost as much as you need them. You will find a whole new way of life here, a life full of people, parties, fun, and love. It is not to be sneezed at at your age. If you need medical help, get it. And don't lie to your doctor. You will not have to fill your empty days with hidden bottles or phony bridge parties. There will be plenty for you to do, helping others, as well as yourself.

I once asked a lady of seventy-five why she bothered at her age to stop drinking. She said, "It gave me back my dignity." Wouldn't you like yours back? And when you sober up, above all refrain from making invidious comparisons between yourself and your friends. What they have and own is theirs. Your comparisons should be made between what you were while you were drinking and what you are now sober. The joy of discovery of your real blessings will be an added boon.

You certainly are never too rich to become an alcoholic. In fact, alcoholism and pill addiction are almost indigenous to the rich. Many rich or very-well-off women drink and take pills because they simply have nothing else to do. They are bored, full of ennui, blasé, have been everywhere and done everything. Their world is artificial and brittle. It is often bounded by the golf or yacht club on the north, department and jewelry shops on the south, the couture on the west, and the hairdresser on the east. How very sad. And this sort of life seems to be on the increase among the too-pampered, spoiled younger generation. If this is the way you want to live, it is your privilege. But in a world full of people with real problems, in a world changing every day, in a world where there is so much to learn, see, and do, I don't think anyone has an innate right to live this way. Too much, too soon may have been your problem; it does not have to remain your problem. Neurosis may be fashionable; it is not easy.

173

# EPILOGUE

The most difficult people in whom to encourage sobriety are the rich. Why should they get sober? The answer is very simple: One day even you must get sick and tired of being sick and tired. And you can give so much, where other busier, poorer women cannot. You have the time, the facilities, the money to help yourself by helping others. All you need is the desire. If you continue to live for yourself alone, and there is really nothing more selfish than alcoholism and its consequent removal from reality, you will die alone—if not physically then spiritually. No one feels sorry for a girl on a yacht. The only way you get people to like you, help you, love you is if you give of yourself—not of your money alone. And the way to do this, if you are alcoholic, begins with not taking that first drink or that first pill. Get out of your silken sheets and extend your hand to someone who needs it. Get sober for your own sake; help someone else for your sake, too. You need it more than they do.

If you are poor, it is easy to drink, to become alcoholic. What have you to live for, you say to yourself. Why should you try; what is ahead for you? The hopelessness and despair of your life settles around you like a shroud. Alcohol is your only escape from hideous reality. Drinking is the way out. If you can afford pills, which you usually cannot, you will take them and drink too. You may have to steal them. Your downward path may take one of two turns: You may slow up on your drinking because you must work, or you may throw it all up and just plan to drink yourself to death.

You may have to make enough money to keep yourself in liquor. This has slowed the progress of the disease for many, but the end is the same. You may get your alcohol through theft, begging, or prostitution.

It is all so unnecessary, so self-defeating. If you don't care about yourself at all, there must be some family you do care about. You will destroy them as surely as if you set fire to their house.

If you have children the only people they will know will be the welfare workers. You have no right to do this to them or to yourself. If life has dealt you a low card financially or environmentally, the way out and up is not in a bottle. You will never, never better yourself by drinking. The money you spend on alcohol can be far better spent on food, clothes, shelter, and education.

Hope in even the lowest springs eternal. If you can hope, you can try. If you can try, you can succeed. You can get free medical help at your local hospital, your local psychiatric out-patient clinic, your state hospital. None of these will turn you away because you have no money. Alcoholics Anonymous is free. Many, many of the women who walk through their doors haven't a penny to their names. All they have is hope. No matter how many problems you have, there isn't one that drinking won't make worse.

You can have a strong motivation for sobriety; chances are you are needed by someone, needed desperately. When you sober up and learn that life is not all bad, you can begin your upward climb. It is exciting; it is rewarding; it is even fun.

You can get a job, a good job, a better job. Perhaps you can even go back to school to finish your education. You can move to a better home, have better clothes, meet nicer people than you ever did in bars. Only you will put a lid on your goals; who knows how far you can go. Isn't a new life, a new beginning promise enough for you not to take that first drink?

You are never too "good" to become alcoholic. Some of the most moral people I have ever known have been alcoholics. You may not be able to face the horrors of real life; you may have been too sheltered; you may believe that life is good, true, and simple. When you discover that evil does exist in this world—perhaps that evil exists quite strongly even within you—you may take to drinking. You are running and running scared. Life was never meant to be like this. What happened?

For you, alcohol and pill addiction, strangely enough, may be the beginning of maturity. You are the ones—the moralists, the idealists—whose remorse, shame, and guilt over your problems will drive you to sobriety. You are the ones whose sobriety will become a shining thing. You will be the leaders, the helpers, the givers. All the goodness, all the joy of life will still be with you. Only now it will be a mature acceptance of reality and a mature acceptance of your role. Out of horror, out of sacrifice comes a rebirth.

Those who have suffered—and no one suffers more than an intelligent, sensitive alcoholic—know the real meaning of compassion, of honor, of giving. You are the ones to whom sobriety is like the sun, rising and shining every day with warmth and life. Don't waste another precious second. Stop hiding your great qualities in a bottle. You have so much to give; the world is truly waiting for you.

So, you are "bad," despicable, beyond help, far gone on the moral-social scale. You might as well drink; no one cares about you anyhow—least of all yourself. You have destroyed everything you touched, everything you loved. Your life is a series of sewers and gutters, literally and figuratively. Alcohol and pills are all that is left to you. For you, it is easy to be an alcoholic.

Don't ever face up for a second; don't look at your life truly; the reality of it is so painful you cannot stand it. Don't be ridiculous! You know there is both good and bad in life. You may very well be bad. You may have been in jail; you may have stolen, slept around, destroyed, even murdered. You may be an outcast, a pariah, unbearable even to your family.

Yet there is hope for you. Stop drinking for just one minute and force yourself to think: Which came first, your "sins" or your drinking? Is one, perhaps, the result of the other? Hundreds of Women in A.A. tell stories far worse than yours; these same women also tell of new lives, of how their troubles began to disappear almost miraculously when they sobered up.

A real destroyer of mankind rarely, if ever, becomes an alcoholic. Such a woman destroys other people; an alcoholic wants only to destroy herself.

An alcoholic, no matter how far gone, is often smarter, more sensitive, more down-to-earth than other women. If you have nothing else to cling to, cling to this. It will help you to get sober. You will still be an alcoholic; only you will be a sober alcoholic. Your good qualities will have a chance to emerge; you will have a chance to start over. How many people get that chance? Yet it is yours for only a telephone call.

No matter how "bad" you think you are, you *can* sober up; you *can* start again. This is the wonderful part of sobriety: You start even with all the "good" girls—with the rich, the educated, the happily married, the conscientious mothers. You may "make it" even before them. You've always been looking for something. How about the challenge of sobriety? Alcohol is the great leveler; sobriety is the great beginning of equality. And, besides, what have you got to lose?

## EPILOGUE

Alcoholism and pill addiction can be evidence of secret death wishes. Sobriety is the love of life—life in all its forms: beautiful, ugly, harsh, cruel, charming, luxurious. The things that made you an alcoholic can make you a great woman, sober. It doesn't matter how you get sober, on whose shoulders you lean, just as long as you stay there. "Hanging in" there can be a great challenge. You are a woman, with a woman's many problems. Yet what real woman doesn't love a challenge. The greatest challenge you will ever have is to stay sober. If you do not, nothing else matters. You will lose it all.

But, if you do stay sober, the rewards will be enormous. You will become truly beautiful, as only those who have suffered and survived can be beautiful. You will see yourself grow and develop as a woman. You will have courage and a sense of humor. You will care about yourself; even more, you will care about others. You will look into your mirror one morning and see reflected there the woman you always dreamed you might be— if you stay sober and work at it. It is to be hoped that you will not merely be "dry," fleeing in terror from alcohol and pills. You will be sober, an entirely different thing. You will be running to meet life, to fling its challenge back in its face. You will live with hope, with joy. And because you have these qualities in full measure, you will be eminently desirable. You will be, truly, a woman.

# Index

## Part I: *You, Too, Can Be an Alcoholic*

179

# INDEX

## Part II: *The Way Out*

# INDEX